Golfing
Breaks

THE COMPLETE GUIDE TO
HOTELS WITH COURSES
IN GREAT BRITAIN & IRELAND

SECOND EDITION

First published in Great Britain 1999 by
BEACON BOOKS
Koinonia House, High Street, Cranbrook, Kent TN17 3EJ.

ISBN 1 901839 28 1

Distributed by The Globe Pequot Press, 246 Goose Lane,
PO Box 480, Guilford. CT 06437-0480.

Cover design by Roland Davies.

Regional introductions by Alistair Tait.

Typesetting Graphco.

Printed and bound in Italy.

Corporate editions and personal subscriptions of any of the Beacon Book guides are available.
Call for details – tel: 0044 1580 720222.

Also published in the series: **Golfing Gems of Scotland**
Golfing Gems of Ireland
Golfing Gems of England & Wales
Golfing Gems Florida
Golfing Gems The Best Links

Contents

Acknowledgements

We are fortunate to have many people working with us who make the task of publishing books like these a pleasure. In particular, we thank Roland Davies for his excellent design skills. The resorts for their assistance, Karen for her excellent organisation and cheery handling of any problems and to Daisy for her enthusiasm. To all of these people we owe our thanks but especially to you for buying the book. Thankyou.

Andrew Finley   *Robert Brand*

Acknowledgements

We offer our sincere thanks to the following for supplying photographs:

Gloucestershire County Council Environment Department
The Heart of England Tourist Board
Southern Tourist Board, photographed by Peter Titmus
The Scottish Tourist Board
The Northern Ireland Tourist Board
The West Country Tourist Board
The Bord Failte – Irish Tourist Board
Isle of Man Tourism & Leisure
The State of Guernsey Tourist Board
East of England Tourist Board Collection
The Wales Tourist Board Photo Library
The North West Tourist Board
The South East England Tourist Board

Welcome

Welcome to *Golf Monthly Golfing Breaks*, the definitive guide to the golf resorts of Britain and Ireland. Our aim has been to provide you with a comprehensive book which will lead you to every hotel which has a golf facility - be it a full-blown championship layout or pitch and putt course.

No charge was made to the hotels for an entry in the guide, however, some opted for an extended double-page feature for which they paid a nominal fee.

Whether your choice is a short weekend break or an extended stay, this book will provide you with a wealth of potential destinations backed with details of the golf facilities on offer and knowledgeable recommendations for classic courses to play in the area. For those non-golfers in the party, local places of interest are included and many hotels provide a host of other activities to keep the golf widow/er amused!.

Other books in the series feature the Golfing Gems of England & Wales, Scotland, Ireland and Florida. All of the courses featured can be found on our website at *www.golfingguides.net.* More books are in production ensuring that with a Beacon Guide, the travelling golfer will never be far from a little piece of golfing heaven.

Happy Golfing!

International Dialling Codes

From UK to Eire	*00353*	*(delete first 0 of local number)*
From Eire to UK	*0044*	*(delete first 0 of local number)*
From USA to UK	*01144*	*(delete first 0 of local number)*
From USA to Eire	*011353*	*(delete first 0 of local number)*

Introduction

R esearch indicates that the number of our readers who take golfing breaks
seems to be increasing on an annual basis. Golf plays an important part in
the lives of Golf Monthly readers and it is a pastime which large numbers
of them are willing to spend a great deal on.

Golf Monthly readers are no different from most other British golfers in as much
as many will cite such destinations as the Bahamas, Mauritius and the States at
the top of their shopping lists. But for the great majority, the choice is closer to
home - and that is not necessarily just a matter of cost.

Britain and Ireland are blessed with an enormous number of great golf courses
and we are fortunate because those courses have an abundance of good hotels to
serve them. It doesn't matter whether it's Aberdovey or Aberdeen, the Cotswolds or
the Home Counties where you want to play your golf, because there is always an
ample choice of excellent hotels to serve a golfer's needs. Some, like those in this
book, have their own courses to offer.

In Golf Monthly Golfing Breaks we have put together a comprehensive guide to all
the hotels available, providing a wide choice for the discerning golfer. There's
something for everyone here and packages to suit all pockets.

Here at Golf Monthly we are serious about our golf and we know that our readers
are too. That's why we have taken a great deal of care putting this edition together
and why we have no hesitation in recommending the facilities contained herein.
We are sure you will enjoy your golf and the rest of your stay.

Kent & The South Coast

Dunorlan Park, Tunbridge Wells

Kent & The South Coast

*N*o less than 13 Open Championships have been held on the Kent coastline. In fact, this coastline was the first area of England to see an Open Championship. The Open was first held in England at Sandwich (now Royal St George's) in 1894 after 33 consecutive years in Scotland.

It was fitting then that an Englishman, John H Taylor, won The Open that year, the first of Taylor's five Open wins.

This part of England was meant for golf. Royal St George's, Prince's, Royal Cinque Ports, the trio make for a fantastic stretch of traditional links golf at its very best. Prince's held the Open back in 1932, when Gene Sarazen triumphed, while Royal Cinque Ports has had that honour twice, in 1909 and 1920.

Strong winds are the main defences of these south-coast courses, because very seldom will you find them on a calm day.

The same can be said of Littlestone and Rye just along the coast. The former is an Open Qualifying course that is currently undergoing renovations to defend it against the onslaught of modern technology. The latter is actually in Sussex and is quite difficult to play unless you are accompanied by a member. So if you know anyone remotely connected with a member of Rye, do your best to nurture the relationship for Rye is the equal of any of the good Kent links.

There's no problem getting onto some of the inland courses in this area, some of which offer excellent golf. For example, courses at Chart Hills and Hever Castle in Kent, and East Sussex National are relative newcomers to the area, but are built to championship standard and conditioning. Nick Faldo is the man responsible for the design of Chart Hills, and a fine job he's done, too. While East Sussex National's two courses – the East and the West – are creations of Robert Cupp, a one time assistant to Jack Nicklaus. East Sussex National's East course was considered good enough to play host for a couple of years to the European Tour's European Open.

To the north of East Sussex National you will find gems in Crowborough Beacon, Royal Ashdown Forest and Mannings Heath. Crowborough Beacon, for example, is a fine example of traditional heathland golf, with good views over the surrounding countryside.

Heading back to the coast you should pay a visit to West Sussex at Pulborough, one of the loveliest courses in the south of England, before heading due south to Littlehampton and its fine links like course.

Further to the west along this coast you will find great golf in Hampshire and Wiltshire. For example, inland from the coast in Hampshire you will be hard pressed to find a better trio of golf courses than Liphook, North Hants and Blackmoor, three that will gladden a purist's heart. In this neck of the woods, or heather perhaps, you will also find Old Thorns and the Army golf club, the former a longish heathland course, the latter a Peter Alliss/Dave Thomas creation in fine wooded countryside.

Towards Southampton you will find good courses in the New Forest in the shape of Bramshaw and Brokenhurst Manor. And if you like golf of the clifftop variety, then pay a visit to Barton-on-Sea. The course isn't too long but the views to the Isle of Wight are worthy of the green fee.

Dorset isn't exactly short of good golf either. While the county has some 30 courses, four are definitely worth highlighting. In Ferndown, Broadstone, Isle of Purbeck and Parkstone, the county has four prime assets. Ferndown has two courses and they are kept in fine condition throughout the year. The golf is heathland in style, so expect heather if you miss a fairway.

The Isle of Purbeck dates back to 1892 and was once owned by Enid Blyton and her husband. The course isn't too long or taxing, but its biggest selling point is the views it offers of this coastline.

Broadstone and Parkstone are courses that fall into the heathland category, with lots of heather and gorse to catch the errant shot. They are a must for anyone visiting this part of the South Coast.

Kent & The South Coast

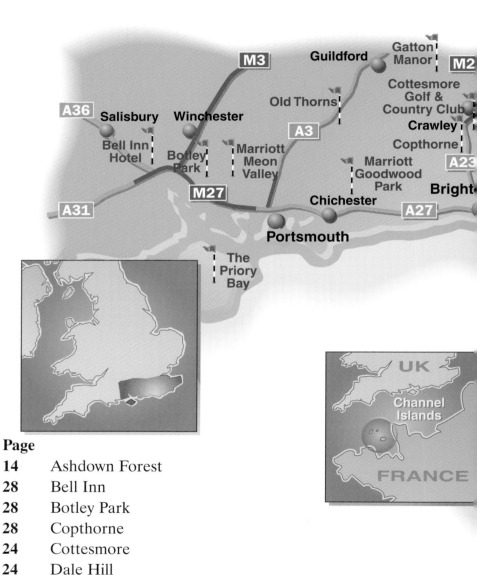

M3
Guildford
Gatton Manor
M2
Cottesmore Golf & Country Club
Old Thorns
Crawley
A3
Copthorne
A36
Salisbury
Winchester
Bell Inn Hotel
Botley Park
Marriott Meon Valley
Marriott Goodwood Park
A23
Bright
Chichester
A27
M27
A31
Portsmouth
The Priory Bay

UK
Channel Islands
FRANCE

Page

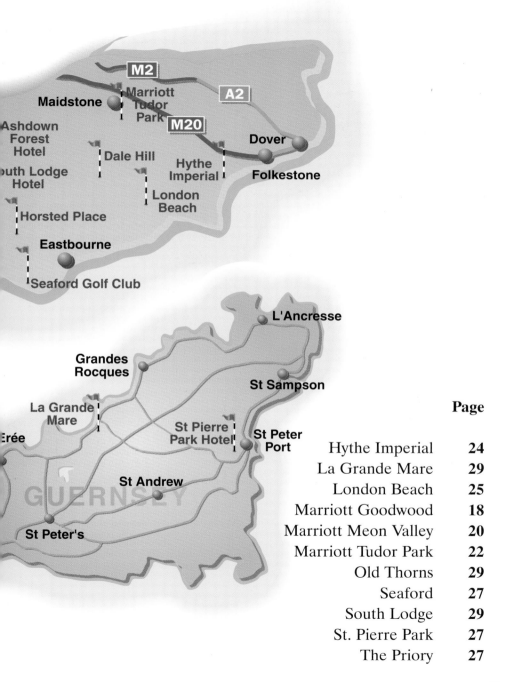

M2

A2

M20

Maidstone

Marriott Tudor Park

Dover

Folkestone

Ashdown Forest Hotel

Dale Hill

Hythe Imperial

South Lodge Hotel

London Beach

Horsted Place

Eastbourne

Seaford Golf Club

L'Ancresse

Grandes Rocques

St Sampson

La Grande Mare

Erée

St Pierre Park Hotel

St Peter Port

St Andrew

GUERNSEY

St Peter's

Ashdown Forest Golf Hotel

*T*he Hotel is idyllically set in Ashdown Forest in the heart of the Sussex countryside and away from main traffic thoroughfares. Each of the 19 bedrooms has ensuite facilities with satellite television, tea and coffee making facilities. The West 19 restaurant is a particular feature, with imaginative dishes and

LOCAL ATTRACTIONS

The Hotel is well located for visits to many famous gardens, historic locations and other attractions. Brighton, the South Coast and Gatwick are all nearby and London is only 40 minutes by train.

vegetarian choices always available. The W.B. Yeats bar, named after the renowned Irish poet who spent his honeymoon at the Hotel, is open for pre-dinner or quiet evening drinks.

Managed exclusively by the Hotel, the Ashdown Forest West Course is adjacent to the hotel complex. Golfers can play the West Course on a daily basis or as part of a golfing break, golf society meeting or event. Constructed in the 1890s and added to in the 1920s, the course was chosen as the venue for the 1932 British Ladies Open. The West Course is not long by modern standards but is a strong test for golfers of all abilities. Tree-lined fairways with small, fast greens will test one's shotmaking. The course has no sand bunkers but the natural terrain is more than ample defence of its par 68, SSS67.

There are numerous other notable courses nearby which we can incorporate into your stay, with reserved Tee Times.

GOLF INFORMATION

18 hole, 5606 yard heathland/woodland course Par 68

Golf Professional: Martyn Landsborough
Tel: 01342 824866

Practice facilities: Outdoor driving range.

Instructions: Groups and individuals catered for.

Hire: Clubs

Green fees by arrangement.

CARD OF THE COURSE

1	386	Par 4	10	450	Par 4
2	153	Par 3	11	311	Par 3
3	352	Par 4	12	122	Par 4
4	270	Par 4	13	357	Par 4
5	156	Par 3	14	435	Par 3
6	328	Par 4	15	388	Par 4
7	240	Par 3	16	196	Par 4
8	312	Par 4	17	502	Par 4
9	353	Par 4	18	295	Par 4
Out	2550	Par 33	In	3056	Par 35

HOTEL INFORMATION

Ashdown Forest Golf Hotel
Chapel Lane
Forest Row
East Sussex RH18 5BB
Tel: 01342 824866
Fax: 01342 824869

Rating: Member American Society of Travel Agents and South East England Tourist Board. Great Golf Hotel Guide Member.
Rooms: 19.
Restaurants: English Food + Vegetarian Options.
Other Sporting Facilities: Riding, Fishing, Tennis and Forest Walks all nearby.

TARIFF

B&B from £65.00 (Single)
£80.00 (Double/Twin).
Dinner + B&B from
£81.50 (Single)
£113.00 (Double/Twin).
No Weekend supplements.

Special Golf Packages:
Golf society packages available on request.

DIRECTIONS

Take the A22 south from East Grinstead towards Eastbourne. Turn left in Forest Row onto the B2110 towards Tunbridge Wells. Chapel Lane is the fourth on the right. Bear right at the top of the lane and the Hotel is on the right.

Gatton Manor Hotel

Set within its own golf course, Gatton Manor Hotel, Golf and Country Club is situated between the towns of Dorking and Horsham in an area of outstanding beauty. The local beauty spot of Leith Hill provides a scenic backdrop to the old Manor House that was constructed in 1729 and was originally the Dower House of the Abinger Estate.

LOCAL ATTRACTIONS

Situated in the heart of the Surrey countryside Gatton Manor is within 15 minutes of the historic market towns of Dorking and Horsham, 20 minutes from Gatwick Airport and just 30 minutes from Guildford. The surrounding area offers beautiful country walks and scenic drives with Leith Hill (the highest point in the South) crowned by an 18th century Gothic Tower providing spectacular views of the South Downs. The Hannah Pascher Gallery is within walking distance and Chessington World of Adventures is only 30 minutes away.

In 1968 when the 18 hole, 6,629 yard, par 72 Championship length golf course was constructed, good use was made of the many water obstacles, ponds, small lakes and streams. As a result water hazards come into play on 14 of the 18 holes. The whole course has character but if one hole was to be highlighted it would be the 18th, arguably one of the best finishing holes in the south.

Gatton Manor is one of the most popular and comprehensive venues in the South of England and offers an entertainment package that is unique in Surrey. The superior Gallery Restaurant offers an extensive à la carte menu and is renowned for its Continental and English cuisine. All hotel rooms are en-suite and have been refurbished to a high standard, retaining many of the features of the 18th century Manor house. The bar, which is open to members and non-members throughout the year, stocks a fine selection of ales, wines and spirits.

The lovely surroundings and the olde world ambience make it an ideal venue to get away and enjoy your golf.

GOLF INFORMATION

**18 hole, 6629 yard parkland course
Par 72**

Golf Professional: Rae Sargent
Tel: 01306 627557

Practice facilities: Outdoor driving range.

Instructions: Groups and individuals catered for.

Hire: Clubs and buggies

Green Fees: Week day – £23.00 Per round,
£40.00 full day. Weekends – £30.00 per round.

CARD OF THE COURSE					
1	435	Par 4	10	178	Par 3
2	144	Par 3	11	271	Par 4
3	413	Par 4	12	377	Par 4
4	174	Par 3	13	501	Par 4
5	479	Par 5	14	176	Par 3
6	369	Par 4	15	553	Par 5
7	187	Par 3	16	432	Par 4
8	510	Par 5	17	585	Par 5
9	443	Par 4	18	402	Par 4
Out	3154	Par 35	In	3475	Par 37

HOTEL INFORMATION

Gatton Manor Hotel,
Golf & Country Club
Standon Lane
Ockley, Dorking
Surrey RH5 5PQ
Tel: 01306 627555
Fax: 01306 627713
Rating: AA & RAC – 3 Star, ETB –
3 Crowns commended
Rooms: 18.
Restaurants: Gallery and Lake Restaurants – English and French cuisine.
Childcare: Childcare can be provided by arrangement.
Hair and Beauty: Aromatheraphy, make-up, body treatments, waxing, manicure, pedicure, massage etc...
Fitness Facilities: Gymnasium and health club includes jacuzzi, saunas and sun bed.
Other Sporting Facilities: Tennis, Bowls, Coarse fishing.
Other Leisure Activities: Assault course (team building events).

TARIFF

B&B twin/double
p.p. £52.50
Single £67.50

B&B+ Dinner:
twin/double p.p. £67.50
Single £82.50

B&B+ Dinner + 36 Holes
from £95.00 to £120.00

DIRECTIONS

From M25, exit at junction 9 – Leatherhead – and take the A24 (signposted Dorking). Stay on the A24 to the end of the dual carriageway, at the large roundabout turn right onto the A29 (signposted Ockley, Bognor Regis). Continue through Ockley (3 miles) and at the far end of Ockley village on the right hand side is a pub called 'The Old School House'; 200 yards past this turn right into Cat Hill Lane and follow the signs. Main entrance is on the right – approximately 2 miles.

Marriott Goodwood Park Hotel & Country Club

Goodwood Park Hotel has been sympathetically created in the grounds of Goodwood House, stately home to the Dukes of Richmond for over 300 years.

The 94 bedrooms are beautifully decorated and include a suite, a 4 poster and 6 Executive Rooms, each offering the very highest standard of comfort and all the facilities anticipated in such a venue. Good food is very much a feature of Goodwood Park Hotel and in the award-winning restaurant you will encounter a wide selection of modern English dishes, all using fresh, local ingredients. For more informal dining, visit the Goodwood Sports Café Bar.

At Goodwood Park leisure facilities are superb, the elegant indoor pool is ozone treated so a dip is doubly invigorating! Alternate lazy lengths of the pool with sorties to the spa bath, solarium, sauna or steam room. Or treat yourself with a visit to the Health and Beauty Salons, or try a workout in the state-of-the-art gym, or perhaps play some tennis.

The grounds of the Estate make a wonderful backdrop for the Hotel's challenging, 18 hole golf course. The course itself is fairly generous over the opening holes and gets progressively harder as you reach the turn. A word of warning though, beware the 475 yard 11th – the deer leap provides a testing obstacle for any golfer foolhardy enough to stray into the ditch with its flint wall. The par 4 17th is aptly named "Ha! Ha!", but whether it's you or the course that gets the last laugh remains to be seen.

LOCAL ATTRACTIONS

Goodwood House boasts a celebrated collection of paintings by Van Dyke, Stubbs and Canaletto, as well as Goodwood Race Course, Aerodrome and Motor Racing Circuit. Chichester, the Norman walled Cathedral City is just three miles away. Other attractions include Arundel Castle, Bosham Harbour and Saxon Church, beaches and nature reserves.

GOLF INFORMATION

18 hole, 6579 yard Parkland

Par 72

Practice facilities: Covered driving range, Tuition & Video facilities

Instructions: Groups and individuals catered for.

Hire: Trolley, buggy & club hire

CARD OF THE COURSE			
1 352 Par 4	10 434 Par 4
2 196 Par 3	11 493 Par 5
3 382 Par 4	12 344 Par 4
4 348 Par 4	13 202 Par 3
5 488 Par 5	14 421 Par 4
6 299 Par 4	15 464 Par 4
7 352 Par 4	16 319 Par 4
8 159 Par 3	17 390 Par 4
9 368 Par 4	18 565 Par 5
Out 2944 Par 35	In 3632 Par 37

SUSSEX

HOTEL INFORMATION

Marriott Goodwood Park Hotel & Country Club Goodwood, Chichester, West Sussex PO18 0QB

Tel: 01243 775537

Fax: 01243 520120

Rooms: 94

Restaurants: Award winning Restaurant, Goodwood Sports Café Bar, Cocktail Bar, Spike Bar.

Beauty: Health and Beauty Salons.

Other Sporting Facilities: Indoor heated swimming pool, spa bath, sauna, steam room, extensive fitness gymnasium and Aerobic studio.

Other Leisure Activities: Tennis courts.

TARIFF

DINNER, BED & BREAKFAST
(Mon-Sun)

Prices start from **£74** per person, per night, including a round of golf. Based on two sharing.

DIRECTIONS

Just off the A285, three miles north-east of Chichester look out for signs to Goodwood and once within the area of the Goodwood Estate you will see signs to Marriott Hotel. Gatwick Airport 50 miles, Southampton/Eastleigh Airport 35 miles.

19

Marriott Meon Valley Hotel & Country Club

*T*he Marriott Meon Valley Hotel & Country Club is surrounded by the Shedfield House Estate, amidst 225 acres of the picturesque Meon Valley in Hampshire.

Following extensive refurbishment the hotel has 113 bedrooms designed to suit all business and leisure needs with facilities such as mini-bar,

LOCAL ATTRACTIONS

The Hotel makes an excellent base for some fascinating sightseeing. Apart from the naval attractions of nearby Portsmouth – the Mary Rose, Nelson's Victory and HMS Warrior, there are numerous other historical points of interest such as the old Capital City of England, Winchester. Those with literary and outside interests can visit Jane Austen's house, enjoy the delights of Marwell Zoo, the beauty of the New Forest, Beaulieu National Motor Car Museum or the Watercress Steam Railway Line.

trouser press, hairdryer, voice mail, fax/modem link and free Sky channels. The Treetops Restaurant has an unrestricted view of the 17th hole of the golf course, which actually has a section of the old Roman road running through it, and both this restaurant and the Long Weekend Café Bar offer a comprehensive selection of carefully prepared dishes.

As with all Marriott hotels, leisure facilities are well provided for and Meon Valley offers, along with the golf and tennis, a heated indoor pool, sauna, spa bath, solaria, dance studio and steam room as well as the fully equipped weights gym and cardiovascular theatre, and a Health and Beauty Salon.

The 2nd and 12th holes on the par 71 Meon Course are a test of anyone's golfing ability, whilst the Valley Course (built around the remains of a Roman village) offers a mature nine holes which present a pleasant challenge for all golfers. Meon Valley has an automated Driving Range which also incorporates the Marriott Tuition Academy where men or women, young or old can benefit and enjoy popular tuition packages offered by the hotels golf professionals. Also available is a comprehensive club and equipment hire facilities.

GOLF INFORMATION

Meon Course, 6520 yards, par 71, 18-hole. Valley Course, 5770 yards, par 70 (9-hole played twice).

Practice facilities: Practice ground with 6 covered bays and putting green.

Instructions: Tuition and video facilities.

Hire: Trolley, buggy and club hire.

CARD OF THE COURSE
Meon Course

1	496	Par 5	10	544	Par 5
2	448	Par 4	11	362	Par 4
3	412	Par 4	12	153	Par 3
4	167	Par 3	13	331	Par 4
5	446	Par 4	14	236	Par 3
6	366	Par 4	15	313	Par 4
7	157	Par 3	16	467	Par 4
8	550	Par 5	17	386	Par 4
9	392	Par 4	18	294	Par 4
Out	3434	Par 36	In	3086	Par 35

HAMPSHIRE

HOTEL INFORMATION

Marriott Meon Valley & Country Club
Sandy Lane, Shedfield, Near Southampton
Tel: 01329 833455
Fax: 01329 834411

Rooms: 113.
Restaurants: The Treetops Restaurant, The Long Weekend Café Bar, Golf Bar, Cocktail Bar.
Hair and Beauty: Health & Beauty Salon
Other Fitness Facilities: Indoor heated swimming pool, sauna, steam room, spa bath, solaria, , free weights gym, aerobics studio, cardiovascular theatre
Other Sporting Facilities: 3 Tennis Courts.

TARIFF

May - Sept £92.00pp DBBG
Mar,Apr & Oct £81.00pp DBBG
Nov - Feb £70.00pp DBBG

Above based on 2 people sharing single supplement £25.00 per night.

Tuition packages from £299.00pp for 3 day package.

DIRECTIONS

From the west, leave the M27 at Junction 7. Take the A334 to Botley. Drive through the village of Botley and continue on the A334 to Wickham. Pass Wickham Vineyard. Sandy Lane is half a mile on your left. From the east, leave the M27 at Junction 10 and take the A32 towards Alton. At Wickham take the A334 towards Botley. Sandy Lane is on the right two miles from Wickham. Southampton Eastleigh Airport is eight miles away.

Marriott Tudor Park Hotel & Country Club

Situated in the heart of the Garden of England the Marriott Tudor Park Hotel & Country Club is merely an hour's drive from London and easily accessible from the motorway network.

Most of the hotel's 120 bedrooms look out either onto the tranquil central courtyard garden or across the beautiful old trees and rolling landscape of the golf course, and all have TV, free Sky channels, radio, hair dryer, direct dial telephone, mini-bar, tea and coffee making facilities, trouser press, iron & board. The Fairviews Restaurant offers an enjoyable selection of fine dishes, or the Long Weekend Bar and Restaurant presents a more informal dining setting.

Leisure facilities available at Tudor Park include an indoor pool, sauna, spa bath, steam room, solarium, aerobics, tennis and health and beauty treatments.

Donald Steel designed a particularly challenging course for Tudor Park. He has cleverly used the natural features of the old undulating Milgate Deer Park, including its many magnificent stands of Scots pines. The par 70 course is 5979 yards long and has a number of interesting holes to test your handicap. The 520 yard 14th for example, is a par 5 and is tree lined on both sides with a slight dog leg to the left. A covered practice ground and putting green are also available.

LOCAL ATTRACTIONS

Besides the countryside with its hop gardens and white-cowled oast houses, a short drive from Tudor Park will take you to such historic castles as Leeds, Hever and Dover, Canterbury with its Cathedral and Canterbury Tales Exhibition, Royal Tunbridge Wells and the historic Pantiles, the famous Brands Hatch motor racing circuit, The Hop Farm Country Park and numerous beautiful gardens open to the public, such as Sissinghurst.
Bluewater - Europe's largest shopping centre is within half an hours drive.

GOLF INFORMATION

Milgate Course, 5979 yards, par 70, 18-holes.

Practice facilities: Covered practice ground and putting green.

Instructions: Tuition and video facilities.

Hire: Trolley, buggy and club hire.

CARD OF THE COURSE					
1	371	Par 4	10	177	Par 3
2	394	Par 4	11	359	Par 4
3	365	Par 4	12	372	Par 4
4	183	Par 3	13	308	Par 4
5	289	Par 4	14	521	Par 5
6	333	Par 4	15	337	Par 4
7	117	Par 3	16	442	Par 4
8	494	Par 5	17	193	Par 3
9	392	Par 4	18	332	Par 4
Out	2938	Par 35	In	3041	Par 35

HOTEL INFORMATION

Marriott Tudor Park Hotel
& Country Club
Ashford Road, Bearsted,
Maidstone, Kent ME14 4NQ
Tel: 01622 734334
Fax: 01622 735360
Rooms: 118.
Restaurants: Fairviews Restaurant, Long Weekend Bar & Restaurant, Leisure Bar, Piano Bar
Hair and Beauty: Health & Beauty Salon.
Other Fitness Facilities: Indoor heated swimming pool, spa bath, sauna, steam room, 2 gyms, Tidro circuit gym.
Other Sporting Facilities: Tennis courts, solarium and aerobics studio.

TARIFF

DINNER, BED & BREAKFAST
(Mon-Sun)

Prices start from **£69** per person, per night, including a round of golf. Based on two sharing.

DIRECTIONS

Leave the M20 at Junction 8 and take the Lenham exit at the first roundabout. At second roundabout take right-hand exit signposted Bearsted and Maidstone. Tudor Park can be found approximately 1½ miles on the left.

COTTESMORE GOLF & COUNTRY CLUB

Buchan Hill, Pease Pottage, Crawley, West Sussex RH11 9AT. Tel: 01293 528256 Fax: 01293 522819

18/18 HOLES PAR 71/69 6248/5514 YARDS

TYPE OF GOLF COURSE: Parkland

GOLF PROFESSIONAL: Calum Callan
TEL: 01293 535399

SPECIAL GOLF PACKAGES:
From £79.00 B&B + EM + 36 holes
Please telephone for details.

Cottesmore is a country club set in 247 acres of unspoilt countryside. The Club was originally a French style farmhouse and has been thoughtfully developed over the years; now offering all the essentials for either a business meeting or a leisure break. Cottesmore features two 18 hole mature parkland golf courses, a luxurious health club, ensuite accommodation and two spacious function rooms. The Club is within easy reach of the major towns of Horsham and Crawley, whilst Gatwick Airport is only four miles away.

DALE HILL

Ticehurst, Wadhurst, East Sussex TN5 7DQ. Tel: 01580 200112 Fax: 01580 201249

36 HOLES PAR DHC 69/IWC 71
DHC 5856/IWC 6512 YARDS
TYPE OF GOLF COURSE: Dale Hill Course: 25 year old parkland course
Ian Woosnam Course: New USGA standard parkland.
RATING: AA 4 Star
GOLF PROFESSIONAL: Andrew Good
TEL: 01580 201800
DB&B + 18 HOLES: £133.00 per person
OTHER SPECIAL GOLF PACKAGES:
Please enquire, usually available throughout the year

Home to the new Woosnam course, Dale Hill is a modern and elegant 4 star hotel with extensive leisure facilities situated high on the Kentish Weald. Many rooms have superb views across the 18th and the surrounding Wealden countryside. Close to the A21, Dale Hill is well situated for London, the coast and ferryports.

THE HYTHE IMPERIAL

Prince's Parade, Hythe, Kent CT21 6AE. Tel: 01303 267441 Fax: 01303 264610
www.marstonhotels.co.uk Email: hytheimperial@marstonhotels.co.uk

9/(18 tee) HOLES PAR 68 5421 YARDS

TYPE OF GOLF COURSE: Links

RATING: 4 Star AA/RAC

GOLF PROFESSIONAL: Gordon Ritchie
TEL: Via Hotel 01303 267441

B&B + 18 HOLES: £85.50 pppn based on 2 people sharing twin/double for 2 nights – unlimited golf

The Hythe Imperial overlooking the seafront is set within its own 50 acre estate with splendid sea, golf course and garden views. The hotel offers 100 individually designed bedrooms including four poster or jacuzzi suites as well as doubles, twins family or single rooms. The leisure centre incorporates the Terrace Bistro and bar providing guests with an informal alternative to the hotel's award winning restaurant. First class leisure facilities include indoor swimming pool, luxurious spa bath with steam and sauna, gymnasium, snooker, squash, all weather and grass tennis courts, putting, croquet and bowls.

LONDON BEACH GOLF HOTEL

Ashford Road, St Michaels, Tenterden, Kent TN30 6SP Tel: 01580 766279 Fax: 01580 766681

Located in rural Kent countryside, the London Beach Golf Hotel provides more than can possibly be imagined for a variety of events or functions with hospitality facilities that are the best in the region.

London Beach Golf Club is the fulfilment of an original idea, that recognised the need to combine the best of golf course design with the highest standard of accommodation and hospitality.

The Hotel will have 24 luxury suites with high tech worldwide communications, including fax and internet connections via the ISDN 30 telephone system.

Every room has en-suite bathroom facilities and private South- West facing balconies overlooking the golf course, King size beds and decorations that will make you want to stay longer.

9 HOLES	PAR 36	2989 YARDS

TYPE OF GOLF COURSE: Parkland

OTHER FACILITIES: 9 hole Chipping course, 9 hole Prcatice putting (mini golf) arena, Golf driving range.

OTHER SPECIAL GOLF PACKAGES:
On application

Scotney Castle, Kent

The Hop Farm, Paddock Wood

THE PRIORY BAY HOTEL

Priory Drive, Seaview, Isle of Wight. PO34 5BU. Tel: 01983 613146 Fax: 01983 616539

The Priory Bay Hotel has recently been refurbished and redecorated to create a unique "Country House Hotel by the Sea".

Among its leisure facilities on its 70 acre estate the Priory Bay Hotel has a 9 hole par 3 golf course set in undulating grounds with outstanding seaviews. An interesting course with no pretensions. Golfers sometimes take 2nd place to the rabbits and wildlife. The hotel also has tennis courts, an outdoor swimming pool and its own private beach, the Priory Bay. The Hotel is a good base to try out the other courses on the island.

There are 18 bedrooms in the main hotel and also a number of cottages on the grounds that sleep 2-10 people. Some of which can be self-catering.

9 HOLES	PAR 3	1307 YARDS

TYPE OF GOLF COURSE: Parkland

RATING: AA 3 Star

RATES: from £50 B+B per person per night based on two sharing. A round of golf is £6.50.

SEAFORD GOLF CLUB

Firle Road, Seaford, East Sussex BN25 2JD. Tel: 01323 892442 Fax: 01323 894113

Dormy House offering twin room facilities for twenty guests. Thirty six holes of golf, room and breakfast, plus excellent five course dinner. One of the finest courses in Sussex, with easy walking despite being situated on the glorious South Downs.

18 HOLES	PAR 71	6651 YARDS

TYPE OF GOLF COURSE: Downland

GOLF PROFESSIONAL: David Mills
TEL: 01323 894160

B&B + 18 HOLES: Full package £70–£95 per person per night.

ST PIERRE PARK HOTEL, GUERNSEY

Rohais, St Peter Port, Guernsey, Channel Islands GY1 1FD. Tel: 01481 728282 Fax: 01481 712041

Set in 45 acres of parkland and lakes, the St Pierre Park boasts two award winning restaurants, a 9-hole Tony Jacklin designed golf course, 3 tennis courts, snooker room and a superb health suite with heated indoor swimming pool, spa bath, saunas, steam rooms, fitness room and a wide range of beauty treatments.

All 132 en-suite rooms are luxuriously appointed with trouser press, hairdryer, colour television with satellite channels, 24 hour room service and tea/coffee making facilities.

9 HOLES	PAR 3	2610 YARDS

TYPE OF GOLF COURSE: Parkland & Lakes
HOTEL RATING: 4 Star RAC & AA, 2 AA Rosettes, 5 Crown Deluxe Guernsey Tourism
GOLF PROFESSIONAL: Roy Corbett
TEL: 01481 728282
B&B + 18 HOLES: From £98.50 (sharing twin/double)
OTHER SPECIAL GOLF PACKAGES:
Golfing break – 2 nts – B&B, 2 rounds of 18 holes, 10% discount in golf shop, pack of 3 golf balls, golf gift and use of Le Mirage Health Suite. £195.00

THE BELL INN
Brook, Lyndhurst, Hampshire. SO43 7HE
Tel: 01703 812214 Fax: 01703 813958
Web: www.bramshaw.co.uk Email: bell@bramshaw.co.uk

	6298	72
HOLES: 3 x 18 **YARDS:** 5552		**PAR:** 69
5506		69

BOTLEY PARK HOTEL, GOLF & COUNTRY CLUB
Winchester Road, Boorley Green, Botley,
Southampton, SO32 2UA.
Tel: 01489 780888 Fax: 01489 789242

HOLES: 18	**YARDS:** 6341	**PAR:** 70

COPTHORNE EFFINGHAM PARK HOTEL
West Park Road, Copthorne, West Sussex RH10 3EU
Tel: 01342 716528

HOLES: 9	**YARDS:** 1822	**PAR:** 30

HORSTED PLACE HOTEL
Little Horsted, Nr Uckfield, East Sussex TN22 5TS.
Tel: 01825 750581 Fax: 01825 750459

HOLES: 2 x 18	**YARDS:** 7000	**PAR:** 72/72

St. Peter Port, Guernsey

LA GRANDE MARE HOTEL
Golf & Country Club, Vazon Bay, Castel. GY5 7LL.
Tel: 01481 56576 Fax: 01481 56532

| HOLES: 18 | YARDS: 5112 | PAR: 67 |

OLD THORNS HOTEL & GOLF COURSE
Griggs Green, Liphook, Hampshire GU30 7PE.
Tel: 01428 724555 Fax: 01428 725036

| HOLES: 18 | YARDS: 6130 | PAR: 72 |

SOUTH LODGE HOTEL & CAMELLIA RESTAURANT
Lower Beeding, Nr Horsham, West Sussex RH13 6PS.
Tel: 01403 891711 Fax: 01403 891766

| HOLES: 2 x 18 | YARDS: 6217/6378 | PAR: 70/73 |

The West Country

St. Michaels Mount, Cornwall

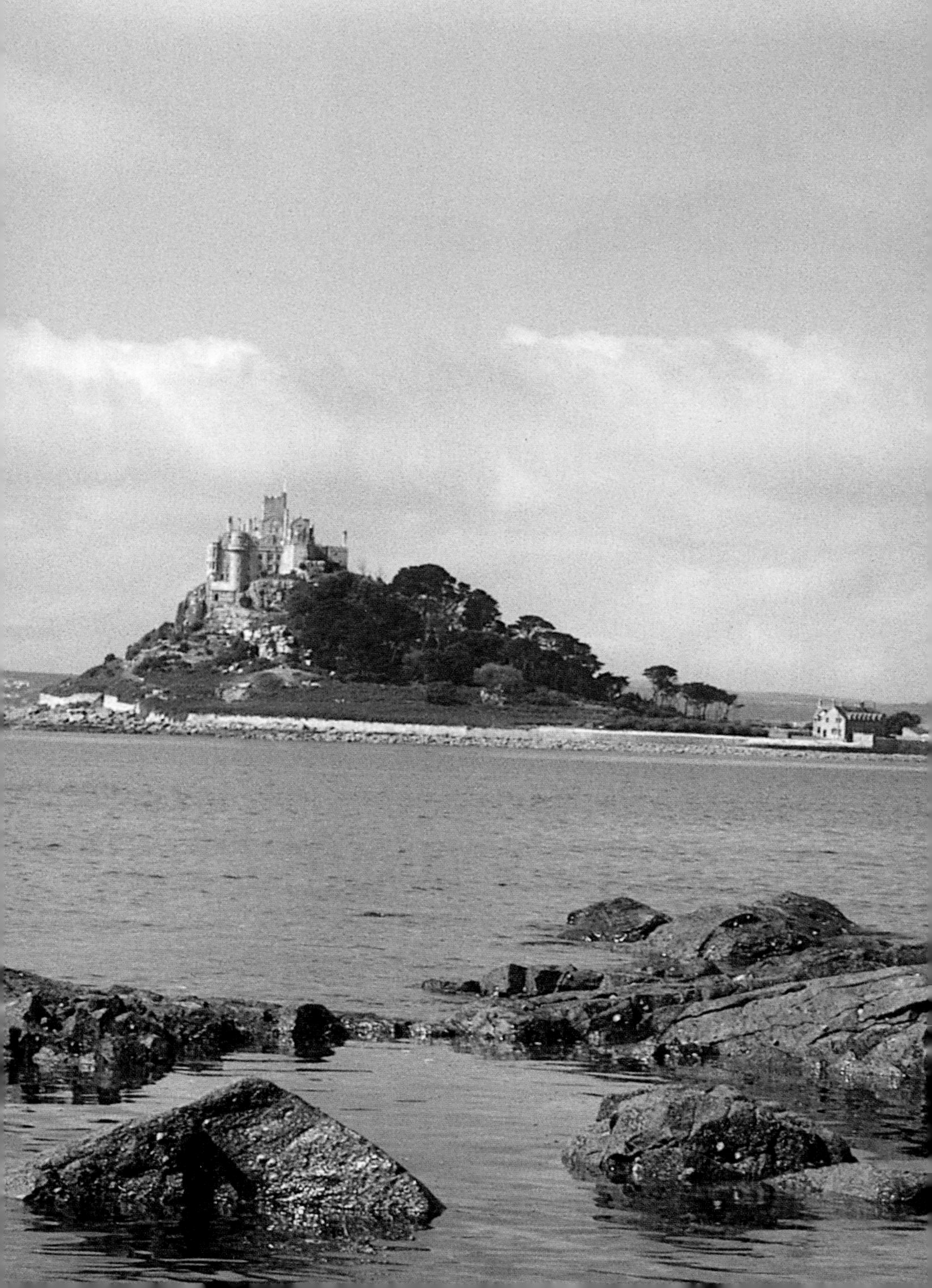

The West Country

*C*lotted Cream, good local ales, long sandy beaches – where are we? The first clue was a dead give away, but then if you've been to Cornwall and the West Country then the latter two may have given you the answer anyway.

There's good golf to be found west of Bristol, down towards Land's End. Links golf, parkland layouts, championship stuff, all located in a place where the rest of the non-golfing family will quite happily let you indulge your passion. The sane ones won't care less how many rounds you play – they'll be too busy lying on the beach or soaking up the charms of the West Country.

All the way back in 1890, a course called Burnham & Berrow was created about one mile north of Burnham-on-Sea, Somerset. Little did they know it, but the man the members chose as their first professional would go on to win five Open Championships. John Henry Taylor was given the job, and it was on the links of Burnham & Berrow that J.H. Taylor found the perfect place to develop the mashie (5-iron) play that was to win him the Open four years later at Sandwich. Quite simply, Burnham & Berrow is one of the finest links courses in the south of England.

Not so far away are to be found two other good links courses, albeit not quite up to the standard of Burnham. Minehead and Weston-Super-Mare are the links in question. Minehead is fairly flat for a links and can get quite busy in the summer. The same goes for Weston-Super-Mare. In other words, don't expect to show up at the height of summer and get a game – phone first.

Mendip is the exact opposite of the two aforementioned links. We go from sea level to a course set up on the Mendip Hills about 1,000 feet above sea level. Good views are the order of the day on this delightful 6,300 yard layout.

Devon is fortunate to have two stretches of coastline, yet the golf on either coast couldn't be more different. Golf on the south coast of Devon tends to be of the clifftop variety, as in the panoramic views from East Devon and Sidmouth, with the latter being quite a bit shorter than the former, by about 1,000 yards. Indeed the only links course on the south coast is to be found at Dawlish Warren on the other side of the Exe Estuary. Here you will find a delightful little links, under 6,000 yards, called the Warren.

If the south coast disappoints in the shortage of links golf, then the north coast more than makes up for it.

The Royal North Devon Golf Club, or Westward Ho! as its commonly called, is the oldest links in England. It also boasts the oldest ladies golf club in the world. As you would expect, this is a truly natural links – so natural that the land is also used by many four-legged creatures. Curious? Well, for years the locals have grazed their sheep on the links of Westward Ho!. Still do. Don't worry, they are well versed in the etiquette of the game, and indeed add a certain charm to your round.

Natural is the way you would describe Saunton, although you won't have to share the fairways with Baa Baa Black Sheep.

Saunton is blessed in more ways than one. It not only has some of the most natural duneland you are ever likely to find, it also has room for two courses, both of them fine links. The East and the West courses are the names given to the two layouts, and of the two the East is the better, measuring nearly 350 yards longer.

Many major amateur events have been played over Saunton's East links. This is a layout to test the very best, and it pays to be long off the tee – eight of Saunton's par-4s measure in excess of 400 yards.

It's not too long a drive from Saunton and Westward Ho! to Cornwall, where you will find another collection of fine courses.

The Duchy also has its own share of good links layouts. West Cornwall, Perranporth, Newquay, St. Enedoc and Trevose are natural links courses that you will want to return to, particularly St. Enedoc, Trevose and West Cornwall.

St. Enedoc's Church course is the older of the two layouts here, dating back to 1890. It's a links that will test every part of your game, a links that's as natural as they come. Trevose is slightly longer than St. Enedoc, although its dunes aren't as large. West Cornwall may be the shorter of the three at just under 5,900, yet its a lovely old fashioned links that you won't tire of playing.

Of course no trip to Cornwall would be complete without a crack at Jack's masterpiece – St. Mellion. For six years the Nicklaus course at St. Mellion was home to the Benson & Hedges International Open. Europe's top professionals didn't exactly find it a pushover, and neither will you. Played over lovely parkland, with several rises in elevation, this is a true championship course in every sense of the word.

Nearby you will find Looe Golf Club, with it's course on high ground where the wind plays an important part in how well you score.

The West Country

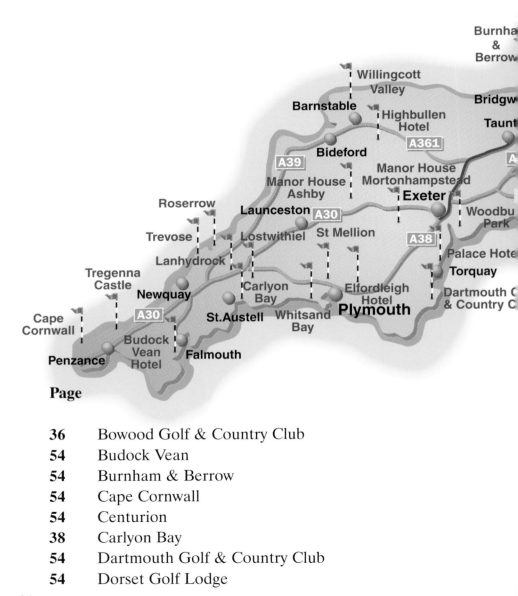

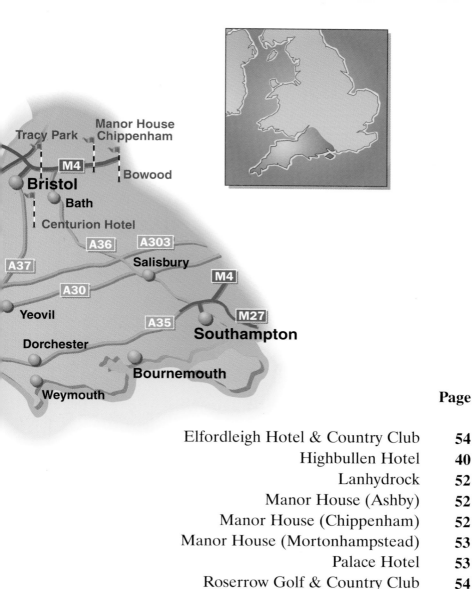

Page

Bowood Golf & Country Club

T Set within 2,000 acre Parkland, Bowood golf course designed by Dave Thomas is widely recognised as being one of the finest in the South of England.

Set between the seventh and eighth fairways of one of the finest 18-hole championship courses in the south of England is Queenswood Golf Lodge. This luxurious Georgian manor house has been furnished to the highest standard throughout by Lady Shelburne, wife of the propietor, with the emphasis on creating the comfort and atmosphere of a private house.

Queenswood is rented out on an exclusive basis, giving you complete privacy in an informal enviroment. The Lodge can sleep up to eight guests and comprises four individually decorated twin rooms (all en suite), sitting room, dining room and study. Great care has been taken over the unique characteristics of each room.

But Queenswood is much more than a lodge - it is a complete experience. After a day of unlimited golf on the Bowood course, you return to the Lodge to enjoy a delicious dinner prepared and served by the lodge Manager and her team. All your menu requirements and wines are pre-selected, so you can simply sit back and enjoy being pampered. You are the hosts of your own dinner party in the charming candlelit dining room and can relax after an invigorating day of golf with first class cuisine and a fine cellar. Once dinner has been cleared, you are left to enjoy your privacy, with the Lodge Manager returning in the morning to serve breakfast. Another day of unlimited golf on the Bowood fairways will leave you looking forword to your next visit.

For the second year running we will play host to the European Challenge Tour. Two putting greens, academy course and floodlit 10 bay driving range, grass teaching facilities.

Activity Centre opening in spring 2000 offering clay pigeon shooting, archery, quad bikes etc.

LOCAL ATTRACTIONS

Places to visit - Bath, Cotswolds, Castle Combe, Lacock, Bradford on Avon and Avebury.

GOLF INFORMATION

18 hole, 7317/6890 yard
Parkland
Par 72

Golf Professional: Max Taylor
Tel: 01249 822228

Practice facilities: Covered driving range.

Instructions: Groups and individuals catered for.

Hire: Golf clubs and buggies available to hire.

Green fees by arrangement.

CARD OF THE COURSE

1	427	Par 4	10	592	Par 5
2	217	Par 3	11	408	Par 4
3	568	Par 5	12	187	Par 3
4	585	Par 5	13	440	Par 4
5	400	Par 4	14	407	Par 4
6	216	Par 3	15	538	Par 5
7	423	Par 4	16	464	Par 4
8	463	Par 4	17	165	Par 3
9	397	Par 4	18	420	Par 4
Out 3696 Par 36			In 3621 Par 36		

HOTEL INFORMATION

Bowood Golf & Country Club,
Derry Hill, Calne,
Wiltshire. SN11 9PQ
Tel: 01249 822228
Fax: 01249 822218
Rooms: 4 Rooms all en-suite.
Restaurants: Servery - traditional hot meals prepared & served by lodge manager (Queenwood)
Other Sporting Facilities: 3 hole academy, driving range, activity centre, including clay pigeon shooting, archery.
Other Leisure Activities: Golf clinic run for children in school holidays, variety of events during year.

TARIFF

Weekend Break
Queenswood Golf Lodge & meals, £34 per round of golf .

Special Golf Packages: Available on request

Other Special Golf Packages: Available on request.

DIRECTIONS

Exit junction 17 off M4. Travel along dual carriageway into chippenham, at roundabout follow signs 'A4 Calne'. Approximately 3-4 miles out of Chippenham follow sign posts to golf club.

GOLF INFORMATION

18 hole, 7317/6890 yard
Parkland
Par 72

Golf Professional: Max Taylor
Tel: 01249 822228

Practice facilities: Covered driving range.

Instructions: Groups and individuals catered for.

Hire: Golf clubs and buggies available to hire.

Green fees by arrangement.

CARD OF THE COURSE

1	427	Par 4	10	592	Par 5
2	217	Par 3	11	408	Par 4
3	568	Par 5	12	187	Par 3
4	585	Par 5	13	440	Par 4
5	400	Par 4	14	407	Par 4
6	216	Par 3	15	538	Par 5
7	423	Par 4	16	464	Par 4
8	463	Par 4	17	165	Par 3
9	397	Par 4	18	420	Par 4
Out 3696 Par 36			**In 3621 Par 36**		

HOTEL INFORMATION

Bowood Golf & Country Club,
Derry Hill, Calne,
Wiltshire. SN11 9PQ
Tel: 01249 822228
Fax: 01249 822218
Rooms: 4 Rooms all en-suite.
Restaurants: Servery - traditional hot meals prepared & served by lodge manager (Queenwood)
Other Sporting Facilities: 3 hole academy, driving range, activity centre, including clay pigeon shooting, archery.
Other Leisure Activities: Golf clinic run for children in school holidays, variety of events during year.

TARIFF

Weekend Break
Queenswood Golf Lodge & meals, £34 per round of golf .

Special Golf Packages: Available on request

Other Special Golf Packages: Available on request.

DIRECTIONS

Exit junction 17 off M4. Travel along dual carriageway into chippenham, at roundabout follow signs 'A4 Calne'. Approximately 3-4 miles out of Chippenham follow sign posts to golf club.

Carlyon Bay Hotel

Stunning sea views from its clifftop position overlooking the beautiful St. Austell Bay await you at Carlyon Bay Hotel.

As a hotel resident, you are entitled to one free round of golf per night of your stay. The 6,500 yard course enjoys breathtaking views where the first nine holes run along the cliff

top before turning inland through beautiful countryside. In addition, set in the hotel's grounds is a 9 hole approach course and a putting green, also free to hotel guests.

The Club House extends a warm welcome to golfers and non-golfers alike. The Club has the benefit of two golf shops, the Pro Shop, open every day for golf equipment, tuition and equipment hire and the Ladies Shop catering exclusively for the lady golfer.

The hotel's Bay View Restaurant offers the best of modern and traditional cuisine. Afterwards, in the comfortable surroundings of the lounge, a variety of entertainment is provided.

In addition to the superb facilities of the hotel we are able to organise a number of outdoor activities including deep sea fishing, horse riding, fly fishing, clay pigeon shooting, yachting and watersports.

The hotel also offers a comprehensive school holiday entertainment programme to cater for all ages along with a playroom to keep the children amused.

GOLF INFORMATION

18 hole, 6578 yard Cliff Top/ Parkland course

Par 72

Golf Professional: Mark Rowe
Tel: 01726 814228
Fax: 01726 815604

Instructions: Groups and individuals catered for.

Hire: Clubs, buggies and trolleys.

Tuition: Available privately or in groups.

CARD OF THE COURSE					
1	385	Par 4	10	514	Par 5
2	467	Par 4	11	151	Par 3
3	192	Par 3	12	350	Par 4
4	516	Par 5	13	516	Par 5
5	191	Par 3	14	336	Par 4
6	368	Par 4	15	531	Par 5
7	364	Par 4	16	400	Par 4
8	372	Par 4	17	387	Par 4
9	350	Par 4	18	188	Par 3
Out 3205 Par 35			In 3373 Par 37		

CORNWALL

HOTEL INFORMATION

Carlyon Bay Hotel
Sea Road, St Austell
Cornwall PL25 3RD
Tel: 01726 812304
Fax: 01726 814938
www: www.carlyonbay.co.uk
email: info@carlyonbay.co.uk
Rating: 4 Star AA & RAC 5 Crowns ETB.

Rooms: 73.
Restaurants: Bayview Restaurant – style modern English.
Childcare: Playroom facilities and Entertainment Programme during school hols.
Beauty: Health & Beauty room specialising in Aromatherapy massage using Epsa Range.
Other Sporting Facilities: Tennis courts, 9 hole course, table tennis, snooker rooms, swimming pools, golf practice ground, Croquet Lawn, Sauna, Spa bath & Solarium.
Other Leisure Activities: Golf Tuition holidays, golf lesson break. Extra golf breaks. Art breaks, wine tasting breaks, flower & garden breaks and shopping breaks

TARIFF

2 Night Break, from £96.00 per person for an inland facing room on DBB terms.

Golf Tuition Courses

5 Day Break Package: from £72.15pp on DBB terms.

DIRECTIONS

At M5 J29, turn left onto M5 for 6.6km, at A38(T) J31, turn right onto A30 for 100.9km, turn left onto A38 for 0.5km, turn right onto Local roads for 2.4km, bear left onto B3268 for 2.1km, go onto B3269 for 2.9km, turn right onto A390 for 7.7km, turn left onto A3082 for 0.5km, turn right onto Local roads for 1.3km, arrive Carlyon Bay, Cornwall.

Highbullen Hotel

*H*ighbullen is a splendid Victorian Gothic mansion complete with parkland, carriageways, home farm and outbuildings.

The hotel stands on high ground between the Mole and Taw Valleys in wooded seclusion, yet with fine views over surrounding country. A spectacular 18-hole golf course is set in the surrounding parkland.

All 44 bedrooms are centrally heated, and have their own private bathrooms. Twelve of these are in the main House.

The restaurant has appeared in all the reputable guides for over 30 years. Light lunches are available in the bar or courtyard every day.

Life at Highbullen is informal and relaxed. We tend to clear breakfast soon after 10am and not take orders for dinner after 9pm but, that apart, there are no rules.

Whatever the season, it's a perfect place for doing nothing, with many quiet hide aways - the drawing room, conservatory and library inside and many secluded corners in the grounds. But if you incline to a more active leisure style you can sample the heated outdoor pool,the squash court, the 18-hole par 68 golf course (5,755 yards) the hard tennis court, or the indoor tennis court, which is floodlit and has an Esco tennis carpeted surface. An indoor swimming pool now occupies the old coach house.

More gentle pursuits are croquet and billiards; sunbed; steamroom and table tennis. Beauty treatments, massage and hairdressing are available by arrangement. There is a comprehensively stocked golf and sports shop.

Over 8 miles of salmon and sea trout fishing are available on the river Taw and Mole, also our private 85 acre semi-natural woodland.

LOCAL ATTRACTIONS

Within 45 minutes of the hotel you have three National trust properties Arlington Court, Killerton House and Knightshayes. As well as Dartmoor and Exmoor National Parks, Exmoor park has several riding establishments.

GOLF INFORMATION

18 hole, 5755 yard Gold course is set in the surrounding parkland Par 68

Golf Professional: Paul Weston

Instructions: Tuition is available.

CARD OF THE COURSE					
1	360	Par 4	10	515	Par 5
2	155	Par 3	11	340	Par 4
3	425	Par 4	12	145	Par 3
4	365	Par 4	13	410	Par 4
5	310	Par 4	14	315	Par 4
6	370	Par 4	15	395	Par 4
7	210	Par 3	16	130	Par 3
8	340	Par 4	17	410	Par 4
9	150	Par 3	18	320	Par 4
Out 2685 Par 33			In 2980 Par 35		

HOTEL INFORMATION

Highbullen Hotel,
Chittlehamholt,Umberleigh,
North Devon. EX37 9HD
Tel: 01769 540561 (4 lines)
Fax: 01769 540492

Rooms: 44.

Fitness Facilities: Heated outdoor pool, Sauna, steamroom, Squash courts, Hard tennis court plus indoor tennis courts.

Other Sporting Facilities: Golf and fishing.

TARIFF

Double/Twin
Mid-week from
£62.50p.p.p.n

Friday and Saturday:
from£67.50p.p.p.n. When occupied by two people this will include dinner, bed and Contnental breakfast.

Single room from £70.00.
Seasonal breaks available.

DIRECTIONS

Take the M5 to Tiverton exit (27), then the new A361 to South Molton. Here take the B3226 Crediton Road. After 5.2 miles turn right up the hill to Chittlehamholt. We are half a mile beyond the village on the left.

Lostwithiel Hotel Golf & Country Club

Lostwithiel Hotel is unique, a hotel and country club of great charm and character. Lostwithiel offers outstanding comfort and service - idyllicly set amongst 110 acres of rolling wooden hills which look down onto the beautiful and tranquil valley of the River Fowey.

The spacious and individually designed bedrooms have been created from old Cornish buildings with their mellowed stone and beamed ceilings. The mood of rural tranquillity is reflected in the country pine furniture. Each room has colour TV, direct dial telephone, tea and coffee making facilities and bathroom.

Dine in style in the Black Prince restaurant where imaginative menus put the emphasis on fresh local produce supported by a carefully selected wine list.

As part of the Leisure Club facilities, the hotel has two all weather tennis courts, a gym and an indoor swimming pool. Activities can include golf, fishing, swimming, tennis and snooker in the sports bar. Excellent salmon and trout fishing can be enjoyed on the River Fowey, bordering the hotel grounds. The 18 hole golf course is one of the most interesting and varied in the county. Designed to take full advantage of the natural features of the landscape, it combines two very distinctive areas of hillside and valley. The challenging front nine rewards you with magnificent views of the surrounding countryside, while the picturesque back nine runs through leafy parkland, flanked by the waters of the Fowey.

LOCAL ATTRACTIONS

The hotel is the perfect base for discovering beautiful coastlines, quiet inland villages, ancient towns and historic houses. Explore the haunting landscape of Bodmin Moor, Llanhydrock House in its fascinating Edwardian timewarp or the Lost Gardens of Heligan.

GOLF INFORMATION

**18 hole, 5781 yard parkland course
Par 72**

Golf Professional: Tony Nash
Tel: 01208 873822

Practice facilities: Covered driving range.
Floodlit driving range with undercover and grass bays,
putting greens and practice bunkers.

Instructions: Groups and individuals catered for +
4 day tuition breaks available.

Hire: Clubs and buggies.

Green Fee (Daily): Low Season £15.00
High Season £26.00.

CARD OF THE COURSE					
1	331	Par 4	10	169	Par 3
2	503	Par 5	11	307	Par 4
3	413	Par 4	12	258	Par 4
4	356	Par 4	13	448	Par 5
5	142	Par 3	14	365	Par 4
6	476	Par 5	15	176	Par 3
7	522	Par 5	16	270	Par 4
8	144	Par 3	17	120	Par 3
9	432	Par 5	18	349	Par 4
Out 3319 Par 38			In 2462 Par 34		

HOTEL INFORMATION

Lostwithiel Hotel Golf &
Country Club
Lower Polscoe, Lostwithiel
Cornwall PL22 0HQ
Tel: 01208 873550
Fax: 01208 873479
Rating: AA/RAC 3 Star. ETB
Rooms: 18.
Restaurants: Black Prince restaurant –
English/French. Sports bar – Traditional pub
style.
Childcare Facilities: Baby listening & sitting by
arrangement.
Fitness Facilities: Gym, swimming pool
(indoor) of 2 all weather tennis courts.
Other Sporting Facilities: Riding and Fishing
available nearby.

TARIFF

B&B + Dinner 1/4 to
31/10 from **£49.00** p.p,
per night.
Winter from **£37.00.**

Special Golf Packages:
DB&B including 18 holes from
£57 Summer or £41 Winter.

Other Special Golf Packages:
Inclusive half board breaks. **Tuition
breaks.**

DIRECTIONS

From A30 take A390.
The hotel is _ mile off the
A390 on the eastern
outskirts of Lostwithiel,
marked by brown tourist
signs.

Tracy Park

*T*racy Park is one of the most beautiful and historic country estates in the Bristol and Bath area. The park, mentioned in the Domesday Book extends to about 221 acres and encompasses two outstanding Championship courses. There are 18 en-suite bedrooms extensively refurbished from the old stables which date back to 1856.

LOCAL ATTRACTIONS

The City of Bath only 4 miles away is the UK's most visited City outside of London. There are great shops and lots of historical interests. Dating back to Roman Times, including the world famous Natural Spring Baths and Pump Rooms. The City will appeal to people of all ages with an abundance of Architectural delights. A City not to be missed.

This delightful courtyard with cottage style accommodation has been sympathetically renovated retaining much of its old character including the original oak beams. Salellite television, tea and coffee making facilities and direct dial telephone are features of every room.

Dine a la carte in our historic restaurant 'Cavaliers Kitchen' with a menu offering an extensive selection of traditional and modern cuisine where you can watch our Chefs create your meal using only the freshest ingredients.

Tracy Park Golf & Country Club is a delightful blend of old and new with a traditional country mansion surrounded by modern golf courses constructed on parkland some 4000 years old. The 36 holes present a challenge to all levels of player with water playing a part on a number of occasions. From the high holes there are magnificent views of the surrounding countryside.

Tuition and practice is never a problem with a 13 bay driving range and our resident professional on hand with the right advice. Tony Jacklin was the original tournament professional attached to Tracy Park.

GOLF INFORMATION

36 hole, 6423 & 6222 yard parkland courses

Par 70 and 70

Golf Professional:
Tom Tompson-Green
Tel: 0117 937 3521

Practice facilities: 13 bay driving range + chipping and bunker areas.

Instructions: Groups and individuals catered for.

Hire: Clubs, buggies at £15.00 a round.

CARD OF THE COURSE

Cromwell Course			Crown Course		
1	523	Par 5	1	562	Par 5
2	210	Par 3	2	428	Par 4
3	355	Par 4	3	440	Par 4
4	406	Par 4	4	165	Par 3
5	178	Par 3	5	390	Par 4
6	390	Par 4	6	135	Par 3
7	295	Par 4	7	389	Par 4
8	430	Par 4	8	422	Par 4
9	490	Par 5	9	401	Par 4
Out	3277	Par 36	Out	3332	Par 35
10	180	Par 3	10	419	Par 4
11	370	Par 4	11	530	Par 5
12	145	Par 3	12	360	Par 4
13	515	Par 5	13	160	Par 3
14	440	Par 4	14	359	Par 4
15	266	Par 4	15	405	Par 4
16	214	Par 3	16	142	Par 3
17	409	Par 4	17	319	Par 4
18	406	Par 4	18	397	Par 4
In	2945	Par 34	In	3091	Par 35

BRISTOL

HOTEL INFORMATION

Tracy Park Golf and Country Club
Bath Road, Wick,
Bristol BS30 5RN

Tel: 0117 937 2251
Fax: 0117 937 4288
www: tracypark.com
email: hotel@tracypark.com

Rating: Highly Recommended.
Provisional 3 Star – Rating applied for.

Rooms: 18.

Restaurants: A la carte with an extensive selection of traditional and modern cuisine.

TARIFF

B&B: Single £49, Double/Twin £65 and Double/Twin Deluxe Suite £85.

Golf: Weekday £15, Weekend £20. These are reduced rates for hotel guests.

DIRECTIONS

The Tracy Park Golf & Country Club is easily accessible from all parts of the South West. From Junction 18 on the M4 it lies 4 miles from Bath, 8 miles from Bristol and 12 miles from Chippenham. The entrance to the course is off the A420, just to the east of the village of Wick. From Bath take the Lansdown Road towards Wick. From Bristol take the A420 east towards Chippenham. From the M4 take Junction 18 then A46 and A420.

Trevose Golf & Country Club

*T*revose golf and Country Club is situated on one of the most beautiful stretches of the North Cornwall coast. It offers an ideal self-catering holiday for the real golf enthusiast or for others who may wish to mix their golf with the other amenities available on the complex or nearby.

LOCAL ATTRACTIONS

3 hard tennis courts, heated swimming pool open from mid May to mid September. Social club membership available. 7 glorious sandy bays within about a mile of the club house, with pools, open sea and surf bathing. Lovely coastline for walking. Convenient for shops.

There are three golf courses. The 18-hole championship course was laid out by Harry Colt who designed, among others, Muirfield, Lytham, Pine Valley, Wentworth and Sunningdale. The 9-hole New Course was opened in 1993 by Peter Alliss who had nothing but praise for its environmentally friendly layout. Measuring over 3000 yards with a par of 35 it is a real test. The Short Course is excellent for beginners, juniors not quite ready for the full course or seasoned golfers who want to brush up their iron shots.

The Clubhouse has an excellent bar & restaurant. There is a snooker room, three all-weather tennis courts and a heated outdoor pool open from mid-May to mid-September. Within a mile of the club are seven sandy bays with bathing, surfing and magnificent coastline for walking.

Accommodation is in 7 chalets sleeping five. 6 bungalows also to sleep five; 13 suites and the Club Flat with three double bedrooms and two bathrooms.

The complex is open all year. Mid-week bookings are encouraged and daily rates are available.

GOLF INFORMATION

18 hole + 2 x 9, 6608 yard Links course
Par 71
Golf Professional: Gary Alliss
Tel: 01841 520261
Instructions: Groups and individuals catered for.
Tennis coaching in July and August.
Hire: Clubs and buggies.
Temporary Membership Fees:
Nov – 21 Dec/4th Jan – 29 Feb: Daily £25, 1 Week £90, 2 Weeks £110, 3 Weeks £135.
22 Dec-3 Jan/1 Mar-30 Jun/8 Sept-31 Oct: Daily £33, 1 Week £135, 2 Weeks £180, 3 Weeks £200.
1 July-7 Sept: Daily £36, 1 Week £160, 2 Weeks £230, 3 Weeks £250

CARD OF THE COURSE

1	443	Par 4	10	467	Par 4
2	386	Par 4	11	199	Par 3
3	166	Par 3	12	448	Par 4
4	500	Par 5	13	507	Par 5
5	461	Par 4	14	317	Par 4
6	323	Par 4	15	327	Par 4
7	428	Par 4	16	225	Par 3
8	156	Par 3	17	388	Par 4
9	451	Par 5	18	416	Par 4
Out	3314	Par 36	In	3294	Par 35

HOTEL INFORMATION

Trevose Golf Club
Constantine Bay, Padstow,
Cornwall PL28 8JB
Tel: 01841 520208
Fax: 01841 521057
Rating: English Tourist Board.
Units: 35.
Restaurants: Licensed restaurant with high standard English Food.
Childcare Facilities: Babysitting can be arranged.
Hair and Beauty: In the area.
Other Sporting Facilities: Tennis, snooker and swimming (in Summer).

TARIFF

**Dormy Flats
(2 beds):** from £47 per night

Special winter rates including:
10% reduction on accommodation rates for any stay of 10 days or more (excluding July/August).

DIRECTIONS

8 miles from Civil Airport. Daily flight to and from London Gatwick.
From London: M4 to Bristol. M5 to Exeter then exit M5 to A30 then bypass Okehampton, Launceston and Bodmin. 4 miles after bypassing Bodmin roundabout at top of hill continue on A30 (signposted Truro, Newquay, Redruth) for about 3.5 miles to a right turn signposted to Padstow (B3274) DO NOT TAKE THIS ROAD but continue for another mile and exit to the right signposted RAF St. Mawgan. After 3.5 miles exit right to Wadebridge on A39. Next roundabout turn left to Padstow B3274. After 3 miles turn left to St. Merryn. After 3 miles you will come to St. Merryn crossroads. Turn left and after 600 yards turn right to Trevose Golf Club and Constantine Bay 1.5 miles.

Whitsand Bay Hotel Golf & Country Club

A magnificent country manor hotel overlooking the ocean and on the edge of a charming and picturesque Cornish fishing village.

The immaculately maintained 18 hole golf course probably commands the best views in the West Country, particularly from the par 3 3rd and 5th which are spectacular indeed.

LOCAL ATTRACTIONS

There are many other amenities locally which include pony trekking, squash, tennis, sea fishing and coarse angling, and 5 other golf courses within a 10 mile radius.

Laid in 1905 by "Fernie of Troon", this is a traditional cliff-top links in the Scottish style. The small greens and undulating fairways with the usual bumps and hollows provide a challenge to both low and high handicapper alike. The lack of trees and exposure to the wind from the sea ensures that all areas of your game will be tested to the full.

The Hotel just 100 yards from the beach, is an impressive mansion with oak panelled Bars, Restaurants and Public Rooms. Bedrooms are comfortably furnished with all the facilities you would expect from a quality hotel. The restaurants are renowned for the quality of their food, created by one of the finest chefs in the region.

The Leisure Centre has an indoor heated swimming pool, toddlers pool, steam room, sauna, solarium and games room. We are able to provide an extensive range of health and beauty treatments. The hotel has its own hairdressing salon, beautician and masseur.

Families are welcome and the general atmosphere is very relaxed and informal. Prices are very reasonable for what is an exceptional hotel.

GOLF INFORMATION

**18 hole, 5950 yard clifftop course
Par 69**

Golf Professional: Steve Poole
Tel: 01503 230778

Instructions: Groups and individuals catered for.

Hire: Clubs and buggies.

CARD OF THE COURSE

1	420	Par 4	10	137	Par 3
2	300	Par 4	11	523	Par 5
3	190	Par 3	12	170	Par 3
4	322	Par 4	13	270	Par 4
5	353	Par 4	14	410	Par 4
6	176	Par 3	15	210	Par 3
7	425	Par 4	16	376	Par 4
8	490	Par 5	17	353	Par 4
9	476	Par 5	18	215	Par 3
Out 3152 Par 36			In 2664 Par 33		

HOTEL INFORMATION

Whitsand Bay Hotel Golf & Country Club
Whitsand Bay
Portwrinkle
Torpoint, Cornwall
Tel: 01503 230276
Fax: 01503 230329
email: carlehotels@btconnect.com
www: www.cornish-golf-hotels.co.uk
Rooms: 40+.
Restaurants: 2 Restaurants serving English & Continental cuisine.
Childcare Facilities: Family sized room with baby listening.
Hair and beauty: Hairdressing salon, beautician & masseur.
Fitness Facilities: Gymnasium
Other Sporting Facilities: Clay pigeon shooting.
Other Leisure Activities: Various special weekends.

TARIFF

From £44 includes
4 course dinner &
Full English Breakfast.
Minimum stay 2 days.

Special Golf Packages:
DB&B – 2 nights approx **£127.50**
Group welcomed - price on application.

DIRECTIONS

From the Tamar Bridge take the A38 approximately 5 miles to Trerulefoot roundabout, take the first exit A374 to Torpoint. Follow road for approximately 4 miles and turn right to Portwrinkle and Whitsand Bay Hotel at signpost.

Woodbury Park Hotel Golf & Country Club

*O*ur new 55 bedroom luxury hotel overlooks the golf courses and reveals stunning views over miles of rolling Devonshire countryside. Here you will find the highest standards of accommodation from deluxe suites to generouly proportioned standard rooms, superb cuisine, luxurious décor, and all set in an atmopshere designed for relaxation.

LOCAL ATTRACTIONS

Killerton – 18th century house featuring displays of clothing and set in beautiful grounds.

Castle Drogo – Lutyens-designed granite castle with elegant rooms and colourful gardens.

Tuckers Maltings – Take a guided tour of England's only working malthouse open to the public.

Kents Caverns Showcaves – Explore the underground world of these spectacular 2 million years old caves.

River Dart Country Park – Country fun for everyone in 90 acres of playgrounds, lakes trails and pony riding.

Lydford Gorge – Enchanting riverside walks leading to spectacular 90ft waterfall and Devil's Cauldron.

Nestled in the woods on the edge of the golf course are the holiday lodges, one has been adapted for the disabled and each lodge is fully fitted with all modern conveniences. Although the lodges are self catering, light snacks and refreshments can be purchased throughout the day and evening in the Clubhouse. Also available is our Restaurant, although booking is necessary. Included in the Lodge tariff is use of the non-chargeable facilities in the Leisure Club.

The Oaks is an 18 hole par 72, 6870 yard course, The Acorns a 9 hole par 33, 2350 yard course. The Oaks is a challenging parkland course with some outstanding holes. The European specification greens are renowned for their quality. The Acorns course is primarily aimed for the higher handicapped player or beginner. The specification and quality of greens is to the same standard as The Oaks.

Pro clinic, video swing analysis and a tour of Nigel Mansell's Trophy room are all available to our guests.

GOLF INFORMATION

27 hole (18 & 9), 6870 & 3204 yard parkland course

Par 72 & 33

Golf Professional: Alan Richards
Tel: 01395 233382

Practice facilities: Covered driving range.

Instructions: Groups and individuals catered for. Computerised video teaching aids. Residential golf schools. Extensive chipping facilities.

Hire: Clubs and buggies.

NB: Handicap certificates required for The Oaks course.

CARDS OF THE COURSES

The Oaks			The Acorns		
1	464	Par 4	1	291	Par 4
2	579	Par 5	2	191	Par 3
3	185	Par 3	3	437	Par 4
4	429	Par 4	4	175	Par 3
5	152	Par 3	5	289	Par 4
6	348	Par 4	6	301	Par 4
7	335	Par 4	7	134	Par 3
8	441	Par 4	8	340	Par 4
9	538	Par 5	9	139	Par 3
Out	3471	Par 36	Out	2297	Par 32
10	377	Par 4	1	308	Par 4
11	455	Par 4	2	208	Par 3
12	423	Par 4	3	486	Par 5
13	412	Par 4	4	163	Par 3
14	469	Par 5	5	280	Par 4
15	243	Par 3	6	292	Par 4
16	486	Par 5	7	125	Par 3
17	366	Par 4	8	295	Par 4
18	168	Par 3	9	128	Par 3
In	3399	Par 36	In	2285	Par 33

HOTEL INFORMATION

Woodbury Park Hotel Golf & Country Club
Woodbury Castle
Woodbury, Exeter EX5 1JJ
Tel: 01395 233382
Fax: 01395 233384

Rooms: 75.
Restaurants: A la carte & Bistro style restaurants.
Beauty: Resident beautician
Fitness Facilities: Indoor swimming pool, fully equipped gym with jacuzzi and sauna.
Other Sporting Facilities: Football pitch, The unique Nigel Mansell World of Racing..

TARIFF

April 2000 – October 2000
All prices are per person on two people sharing Standard, Double or Twin. Minimum 4 people in party.

Golf & Leisure Rates
Dinner, Bed & Breakfast and 18 holes.
Weekday (Sun-Thurs) **£99.00**
Weekends (Fri-Sat) **£109.00**

Non Golfers in Party
Dinner, Bed & Breakfast and free use of Leisure Club.
Weekday **£80.00**
Weekends **£85.00**

DIRECTIONS

Woodbury Park Golf & Country Club is fully signposted by AA road signs and is easy to find. Leave M5 at Junction 30 and follow A376 to Sidmouth/Exmouth. Then A3052 to Sidmouth until you reach the Halfway House Inn on your left. Turn right on the B3180 to Budleigh Salterton and continue onto Woodbury Common. Woodbury Park Golf Course is signposted clearly on your right hand side.

LANHYDROCK GOLFING LODGE

Lostwithiel Road, Bodmin, Cornwall PL30 5AQ. Tel: 01208 73600 Fax: 01208 77325
Web: http://www.lanhydrock-golf.co.uk Email: golfbreaks@lanhydrock-golf.co.uk

18 HOLES	PAR 70	6100 YARDS

TYPE OF GOLF COURSE: Parkland

GOLF PROFESSIONAL: Jason Broadway
TEL: 01208 73600

OTHER SPECIAL GOLF PACKAGES:
D.B.B + unlimited golf from £64

Lanhydrock Golfing Lodge is located only 100 yards from the main clubhouse where all meals are taken. Featured in our sister publication "Golfing Gems" the course is a beautiful parkland design with lakes, trees and wide bunkers to test all standards. The lodge sleeps up to 9 people and will accept a minimum of 4.

MANOR HOUSE & ASHBURY HOTELS

Fowley Cross, Okehampton, Devon EX20 4NA. Tel: 01837 53053/01837 55453
Fax: 01837 55027/01837 55468 Web: www.manorhousehotel.co.uk

Ashbury 27/Oakwood 18 HOLES
PAR 70/68   5881/5244 YARDS
TYPE OF GOLF COURSE: Rolling countryside
GOLF PROFESSIONAL: Reg Cade
TEL: 01837 55453
B&B + 18 HOLES: 3 nights £133/156 – £176/193. Approx prices Nov 2000 – July 2000
OTHER SPECIAL GOLF PACKAGES:
Party Discounts/Bargain Breaks

Two country house hotels offering superb views, service and food. 27 hole course (3x9's) 18 hole course; 18 hole par3 course. Free golf on 3 night stays. Driving range, buggies, golf tuition. Unique craft centre – full daily tuition, pottery, candles, glass engraving, enamelling, painting and sketching. Heated indoor pools, sauna, squash, badminton, snooker, archery, laser clays, bowls, tennis, all indoors and free. Outdoor bowls, tennis, guided moor walks – all free. Evening entertainment includes line dancing, skittles, music for all ages, 'casino' and quiz.

MANOR HOUSE HOTEL

Castle Combe, Chippenham, Wiltshire SN14 7HR. Tel: 01249 782206 Fax: 01249 782159

18 HOLES	PAR 72	6286 YARDS

TYPE OF GOLF COURSE: Parkland
RATING: 4 Red Stars AA – RAC Gold Ribbon.
GOLF PROFESSIONAL: Chris Smith
TEL: 01249 783101
B&B + 18 HOLES: £221 x 2 people
OTHER SPECIAL GOLF PACKAGES:
£150 per person per night – 2 nights minimum.

15th century manor house nestling in wooded valley on the southern edge of the Cotswolds. Exceptional standard of comfort and hospitality; award-winning food. Spectacular and challenging championship golf course designed by Peter Alliss and rated one of the finest inland courses in the country.

MANOR HOUSE HOTEL & GOLF COURSE

Moretonhampstead, Devon TQ13 8RE. Tel: 01647 440355 Fax: 01647 440961

The Manor House Hotel is an imposing Jacobean style mansion set in 270 acres on the edge of Dartmoor. It's 90 bedrooms are complimented by lounges, bars and The Hambleden Restaurant. Also on site are tennis, croquet, fishing and snooker. Golf breaks for couples, groups and societies available throughout the year.

18 HOLES	PAR 69	6016 YARDS
TYPE OF GOLF COURSE: Parkland		
HOTEL RATING: AA 4 Star – RAC 4 Star AA Rosettee		
GOLF PROFESSIONAL: Richard Lewis **TEL:** 01647 440998		
B&B + 18 HOLES: From £69.00 p.p.p.n.		
OTHER SPECIAL GOLF PACKAGES: Half Board inc golf from £79.00 p.p.p.n.		

Bowemans Nose, Dartmoor

PALACE HOTEL

Babbacombe Road, Torquay TQ1 3TG. Tel: 01803 200200 Fax: 01803 299899
Web: www.palacetorquay.co.uk

The Palace Hotel offers for your enjoyment a superb 9 hole championship golf course, set within mature wooded grounds offering challenging features including ponds and streams. The Palace Hotel is an independent four-star hotel which in addition to the golf course offers indoor and outdoor tennis courts and swimming pools, squash courts, snooker rooms and croquet lawn.

9 HOLES	PAR 3	710 YARDS
TYPE OF GOLF COURSE: Short Championship Course		
RATING: 4 Star RAC/AA		
GOLF PROFESSIONAL: Bob Bradbury		
B&B + 18 HOLES: £61.00		

BUDOCK VEAN GOLF & COUNTRY HOUSE HOTEL
Helford River, Mannan Smith, Falmouth, Cornwall TR11 5LG.
Tel: 01326 250 288 Fax: 01326 250892

HOLES: 9/18 **YARDS:** 2657/5153 **PAR:** 34/68

BURNHAM & BERROW GOLF CLUB
St. Christopher's Way, Burnham-on-Sea, Somerset TA8 2PE.
Tel: 01278 785760 Fax: 01278 795440

HOLES: 9/18 **YARDS:** 6606/6332 **PAR:** 71/72

CORNWALL GOLF & COUNTRY CLUB LTD
Cape Cornwall, St Just. Penzance, Cornwall, TR19 7NL.
Tel: 01736 788611 Fax: 01736 788611

HOLES: 18 **YARDS:** 5462 **PAR:** 70

CENTURION HOTEL
Charlton Lane, Midsomer Norton, Bath BA3 4BD.
Tel: 01761 417711 Fax: 01761 418357

HOLES: 9 **YARDS:** 2139 **PAR:** 40

DARTFORD GOLF & COUNTRY CLUB
Dartmouth Golf & Country Club, Blackawton, Totnes
Devon. TQ9 7DE
Tel: 01803 712650 Fax: 01803 712628

HOLES: 18/9 **YARDS:** 6663/5166 **PAR:** 72/65

DORSETSHIRE GOLF LODGE
Bere Regis, Wareham, Dorset BR20 7NT
Tel: 01929 472244 FAX: 01929 471294

HOLES: 18 **YARDS:** 6580 **PAR:** 72

ELFORDLEIGH GOLF CLUB
Colebrook, Plymouth, Plymouth PL7 5EB.
Tel: 01752 336428 Fax: 01752 344581

HOLES: 9/(18tees) **YARDS:** 5210 **PAR:** 68

ROSERROW GOLF & COUNTRY CLUB
St Minver, Wadebridge, Cornwall. PH27 6QT.
Tel: 01208 862424 Fax: 01208 862218

HOLES: 18 **YARDS:** 6651 **PAR:** 72

ST. MELLION HOTEL GOLF & COUNTRY CLUB

St Mellion, Nr Saltash, Cornwall PL12 6SD.
Tel: 01579 351351 Fax: 01579 350537

HOLES: 36   **YARDS:** 6651/5782   **PAR:** 72/68

TREGENNA CASTLE HOTEL

St Ives, Cornwall TR26 2DE.
Tel: 01736 795254 Fax: 01736 796066

HOLES: 18   **YARDS:** 3478   **PAR:** 60

WILLINGCOTT VALLEY GOLF & LEISURE COMPLEX

Willingcott, Woolacombe, North Devon EX34 7HN.
Tel: 01271 870173 Fax: 01271 870800

HOLES: 9(18Tee) **YARDS:** 6012 **PAR:** 69

Shaftesbury (N. Dorset)

The Midlands

Longborough, Gloucestershire

The Midlands

*T*he heart of England is fine proof that you don't have to go to the sea to find great golf courses. In England's green and pleasant land you will find enough parkland courses to make you want to return year after year.

Where better to start than in Lincolnshire? It is in this county that you will find perhaps the greatest inland course in all of England, perhaps in the whole of the British Isles.

A few years ago the American magazine Golf Digest compiled its top 100 courses in the world. Pine Valley in New Jersey came out top, and many fine links courses featured high up the list. Top British inland course was Woodhall Spa, an excellent accolade considering it was up against the likes of Gleneagles, Ganton and Sunningdale.

Harry Vardon originally laid out this course in 1905, but alterations were later made by Harry Colt of Wentworth fame, and by Colonel Hotchkin. What they created was a classic heathland course, one with lots of heather, trees and fairways sitting on lovely sandy subsoil. This classic course measures just short of 7,000 yards and what you will probably remember most about it are the huge gaping bunkers. A course not to be missed.

Golf of the heathland variety can also be found over in Nottinghamshire. Notts Golf Club, or Hollinwell as its also known, Coxmoor and Sherwood Forest provide a trio of heathland/moorland courses the county can be proud of.

Derbyshire isn't known for its great golf courses, but there are some little gems to be found. Buxton and High Peak and Cavendish certainly fall into that category. Both are to be found in the town of Buxton in some of the loveliest countryside in England. Other good courses in Derbyshire include Kedelston Park and Breadsall Priory near Derby. The former is a located in a beautiful setting while the latter is a golf and country club established in 1976.

Like Derbyshire, Leicestershire is not known for its great golf courses but it does contain one classic heathland gem, in the shape of Luffenham Heath. While not in the same league as, say, Woodhall Spa, Luffenham is a joy to play. Another joy can be found at Longcliffe, a heavily wooded course that requires you to hit the ball straight.

Of course the Midlands is the scene of one of the most famous golf events ever. It was at The Belfry, near Birmingham, in 1985 that Europe finally wrested the Ryder Cup from the Americans after years of losing. That event, and subsequent matches in 1989 and 1993 put The Belfry on the map. Everyone wants to play the courses two signature holes, the 10th and the 18th. Just don't expect to play them well.

Little Aston is another course associated with Birmingham. It's one known for its greens and its superb conditioning. One you should play if you get the chance. Other courses near Birmingham that have to be played include Fulford Heath, Kings Norton and Copt Heath, all to the south of the city.

A good addition to Midlands golf in recent years has been the Forest of Arden. Now owned by the Marriott hotel group, this course is now a regular venue on the PGA European Tour.

Just south of the Forest of Arden and Coventry, at Warwickshire, is to be found a new American style 36-hole complex called The Warwickshire. Comprising four separate nines, the holes have been built to a very high standard and provide a strong challenge.

Nearby in Stratford upon Avon are to be found two good courses at Stratford and the Welcombe Hotel. Both offer a pleasant day's golf, and the latter recently hosted an event on the European Seniors Tour.

In the extreme west Midlands, in Shropshire, you will find a collection of good courses that can provide several days of good golf. This little county beside the Welsh border has produced a number of fine golfers over the years – Ian Woosnam, Sandy Lyle and Peter Baker to name but three. Lyle learned his golf at Hawkstone Park, while Woosnam played as a lad at Llanymynech, a course where one hole, the 4th, calls for a tee shot to be played in Wales to a green that lies in England. Good golf is also to be found at Hill Valley.

To the north of Shropshire lies the county of Cheshire and the golf there is nothing to be sneezed at either. Mere, Delamere Forest, Sandiway, Mottram Hall, Carden Park and Portal are all worthy of a visit, especially Portal. This championship course near Tarporley lies in lovely parkland and offers a strong challenge to even the lowest of handicaps.

Midlands & Cotswolds

Kingston upon Hull

Forest Pines (Briggate Lodge)

:unthorpe

Grimsby

A16

Grange & Links Hotel

A158

Lincoln

North Shore

A52

Boston

17

elton Woods

Grantham

House

Peterborough

ring

Bank House Hotel Golf & Country Club

*T*he delightful Hotel and golf course here at Worcester has been open for six years in 123 acres of the Worcestershire countryside.

Set against the backcloth of the Malvern Hills, the course is 6,204 yards, par 72, designed on a 'Florida' style. It is flat, with mounded fairways, dog legs and two island greens. Numerous lakes/water hazards provide both a challenge and scenic beauty for all

LOCAL ATTRACTIONS

The Hotel is well located for visits to many famous gardens, historic locations, such as Worcester Cathederal, Worcester Porcelain & Pottery, Worcester Commandary, Malvern Hills and Malvern theatre.

types of golfer. We have a 20 bay driving range, a short game practice area and putting green. The Club House, changing rooms,and Pro-Shop are situated approximately 200yds from the Hotel near the golf course. Residential golfers may use the Clubhouse, but dinner is served in the Hotel in the evening.

The Hotel is ideally suited for both business and pleasure. Farthings Restaurant is a splendid setting to enjoy fine cuisine and wines from around the world. All food is freshly cooked by our team of chefs, offering a wide variety to satisfy any palate.

After your meal you can enjoy a drink in the Exchange Bar with 17th Century Oak beams and an original inglenook fireplace. If you prefer a more informal meal, an excellent selection of bar meals are served both at lunchtimes and in the evening.

The Hotel has 70 ensuite Bedrooms, tastefully decorated for the discerning guest. Including Four-poster and Bridal Suite, Executive, Ladies and Standard rooms with non-smoking rooms available.

For the health conscious the hotel offers excellent leisure facilities including spa pool, sauna, high tanning sunbed, gymnasium and outdoor swimming pool.

GOLF INFORMATION

**18 hole, 6204 yard
Florida style course with 14 lakes.
Par 72**

Golf Professional: Craig George
Tel: 01886 833545

Practice facilities: Driving range (20 bays) short game practice areaand putting green.

Instructions: Groups and individuals catered for.

Hire: Golf Cars (buggies) book in advance.

Green fees by arrangement.

CARD OF THE COURSE

1	357	Par 4	10	333	Par 4
2	366	Par 4	11	185	Par 3
3	180	Par 3	12	480	Par 5
4	490	Par 5	13	163	Par 3
5	190	Par 3	14	525	Par 5
6	481	Par 5	15	160	Par 3
7	188	Par 3	16	333	Par 4
8	488	Par 5	17	403	Par 4
9	378	Par 4	18	504	Par 5
Out	**3118**	**Par 36**	**In**	**3986**	**Par 36**

HOTEL INFORMATION

Bank House Hotel Golf & Country Club
Tel: 01886 833545
Fax: 01886 832461
Rating: AA three star, English tourist Board four crowns highly commended.
Rooms: 70 Rooms all en-suite.
Restaurants: Restaurant full a la carte & table d'hote.
Other Sporting Facilities: Fitness centre, sauna, jacuzzi, sunbed, outdoor swimming pool.
Other Leisure Activities: Conference facilities for up to 350 delegates.

TARIFF

Weekend Break
Two nights Dinner, room & breakfast. Golf, full use of fitness centre, sauna and Spa Pool. £155 per player, sharing a twin/double.
Midweek Break
Two nights. Dinner, room & breakfast. 3 rounds of golf, £150 per player.
One nights. Dinner, room & breakfast. 2 rounds of golf, £80 per player.

Special Golf Packages:
Available on request.

Other Special Golf Packages:
Available on request.

DIRECTIONS

From Junction 7 M5 follow signs to Worcester West, Malvern and Ross. Then pick up signs for Hereford on the A4440 which takes you to the A4103 Hereford Road. Turn left, signposted Hereford, and hotel is approximatley 2 miles on left hand side off the roundabout. The Journey time from junction 7 is approximatley 15 minutes. The nearest airport is Birmingham International Airport (35 miles) and the nearest mainline British Rail Station is Shrub Hill, Worcester (3 miles).

The Belfry

The Belfry is set in 500 acres of North Warwickshire countryside. It is in the centre of the country, close to the M42 motorway and only ten minutes drive from Birmingham International airport and station.

The Belfry's famous fairways and greens are known to golfers throughout the world. The Belfry is unique as the only venue to have staged the biggest golf event in the world – The Ryder Cup Matches – an unprecedented 3 times with a 4th returning in 2001. The Brabazon is regarded throughout the world as a great championship course with some of the most demanding holes in golf. A £2.4million redevelopment made it even more challenging and atttractive; holes, lakes and streams have been reshaped and several holes have been given a dramatic new look. Famous holes like the 10th (Ballesteros's hole), and the 18th, with its amphitheatre final green, will of course remain as they were.

For those who like their golf a little easier, The Derby course is ideal and can be played by golfers of any standard. Alternatively, The PGA National Course, designed by Dave Thomas is a challenge and has been used for professional competition.

The Belfry Resort is made up of a 324 bedroom 4-star hotel, 21 conference and meeting rooms, 5 restaurants and 8 bars. There is a Leisure Club and The Bel Air Nightclub in the hotel grounds.

LOCAL ATTRACTIONS

Warwick Castle, Cadbury World and the acclaimed Symphony Hall in Birmingham and the city's exciting shopping, are within easy reach. However, for extra excitement, residents receive complimentary entry to one of Britain's most popular amusement parks Drayton Manor Family Theme Park (excluding Bank Holiday Mondays). There are plenty of other local attractions and tickets for many local places of interest can be purchased from reception.

GOLF INFORMATION

3 x 18 holes, 7118 yard (The Brabazon at The Belfry), 7053 yard (PGA National Course) 6009 (Derby Course).

Par 72 (The Brabazon at The Belfry), 72 (PGA) and 69 (Derby).

Golf Professional: Peter McGovern

Tel: 01675 470301

Practice facilities: Covered driving range and putting green

Instructions: Groups and individuals catered for and full team of PGA Qualified golf professionals.

Hire: Clubs, buggies and trollies.

Green Fees to 31/10/00 The Brabazon at The Belfry £90 – PGA National £60 – Derby £30.

Winter Green Fees on request.

CARD OF THE COURSE

The Brabazon			PGA National		
1	411	Par 4	1	353	Par 4
2	379	Par 4	2	538	Par 5
3	538	Par 5	3	196	Par 3
4	442	Par 4	4	405	Par 4
5	408	Par 4	5	448	Par 4
6	395	Par 4	6	522	Par 5
7	177	Par 3	7	464	Par 4
8	428	Par 4	8	224	Par 3
9	433	Par 4	9	443	Par 4
Out	3611	Par 36	Out	3593	Par 36
10	311	Par 4	10	502	Par 5
11	419	Par 4	11	209	Par 3
12	208	Par 3	12	562	Par 5
13	384	Par 4	13	419	Par 4
14	190	Par 3	14	439	Par 4
15	545	Par 5	15	195	Par 3
16	413	Par 4	16	350	Par 4
17	564	Par 5	17	384	Par 4
18	473	Par 4	18	400	Par 4
In	3507	Par 36	In	3460	Par 36

HOTEL INFORMATION

The Belfry
Wishaw, North Warwickshire B76 9PR
Tel: 01675 470033
Fax: 01675 470256
Rating: 4 Star
Rooms: 324.
Restaurants: 5 Restaurants inc.

The Atrium Restaurant, Riley's Conservatory Restaurant and bar, The French Restaurant holder of 2 AA rosettes, Leisure Club cafe.
Childcare: Baby Monitoring and Child Listening Service.
Hair and Beauty: Hair Salon and Beauty Treatments available
Fitness Facilities: Fully equipped Leisure Club with swimming pool, gym, aqua spa, sauna and whirlpool.
Other Sporting Facilities: Squash, Snooker, Jogging Trail, Tennis, Putting green, Driving Range. Any on-site activity by arrangement.

TARIFF

Breaks at the Belfry 'a la carte'
At the Belfry breaks are as individual as our guests and you can make up your break from the 'A la carte' selection allowing you to tailor make a break that suits your individual requirements. The Belfry breaks(*) are per person per night sharing a twin/double standard Belfry room and full English Breakfast.

	Residential		Residential	Non-Residential
		Dinner (Atruim/Riley's)	£23.95	£19.00
*Belfry Breaks	£70.00	Dinner (French Table d'Hote)	£25.00	£32.00
*Belfry Breaks Special	£50.00	Leisure Club Pass	£10.00	£40.00
*Sunday Specials	£35.00	PGA National Green Fees	£40.00	£20.00
		Derby Course Green Fees	£15.00	£20.00

DIRECTIONS

Leave M42 at Junction 9 and follow signs for Lichfield along the A446. The Belfry is one mile on the right.

Carden Park Hotel , Golf Resort & Spa

arden Park, a golf resort that ranks alongside the best in the world, is set in 750 acres of beautiful countryside. The golf facilities are unrivalled in Great Britain and include the magnificent Nicklaus course - a resort style with 5 tee positions on each hole to provide challenging enjoyment for everyone, the 18 hole championship Cheshire course, the 9 hole Par 3 Azalea course and Europe's first

Jack Nicklaus residential golf school. The golf school with its team of Nicklaus/Flick accredited teaching pros caters for everyone from complete beginners to scratch players.

Visitors have use of a unique range of facilities for learning, practising and improving golf including the all weather driving range with fully landscaped target area, an extensive short game practice area and putting greens. Inside is a theatre for group tuition, computerised video equipment for individual instruction, an indoor putting course and golf simulators where you can test your skills on the world's best courses.

The luxurious AA/RAC 4 Star hotel with its 192 bedrooms and suites offers an interesting range of dining options to suit your mood. Carden also has an extensive Spa with 20 metre pool, wet and dry relaxation areas, gymnasium, dance studio and 15 individual treatment rooms for the ultimate in pampering. Other leisure activities on the estate include croquet, tennis, mountain biking and horse riding. Carden Park offers a wide range of golf packages including playing and tuition, as well as interesting options for non golfers that include use of the superb spa.

LOCAL ATTRACTIONS

Being only 30 mins from junction 16 of M6 and 15 mins from the historic town of Chester, Carden Park is ideally located for exploring the many attractions and great days out that are available in the area. The Carden Estate nestles between contrasting and beautiful landscapes of the Cheshire Plain and Welsh Hills, from picturesque black and white buildings, delightful gardens, sweeping hills and historic towns there is something for everyone. And nearby you will find Chester Zoo, Chester Races and Oulton Park, Beeston, Peckforton and Chirk Castles, the Cheshire cheese experience, Cheshire military museum and Stretton Water Mill.

GOLF INFORMATION

45 hole, The Nicklaus course 7010 yard, The Cheshire course 6891 yard, all mature parkland with challenging water features.

Par Nicklaus 72 & Cheshire 72

Golf Professional: David Llewellyn
Tel: 01829 731600

Practice facilities: Covered driving range.

Instructions: Groups and individuals catered for, plus Jack Nicklaus residential golf school.

Hire: Clubs and buggies.

CARD OF THE COURSE

The Nicklaus			The Cheshire		
1	428	Par 4	1	355	Par 4
2	319	Par 4	2	569	Par 5
3	172	Par 3	3	461	Par 5
4	522	Par 5	4	397	Par 4
5	426	Par 4	5	190	Par 3
6	353	Par 4	6	273	Par 4
7	398	Par 4	7	165	Par 3
8	153	Par 3	8	363	Par 4
9	549	Par 5	9	335	Par 4
Out	3320	Par 36	Out	3108	Par 36
10	406	Par 4	10	165	Par 3
11	430	Par 4	11	559	Par 5
12	219	Par 3	12	350	Par 4
13	547	Par 5	13	372	Par 4
14	338	Par 4	14	370	Par 4
15	393	Par 4	15	539	Par 5
16	136	Par 3	16	424	Par 4
17	352	Par 4	17	217	Par 3
18	487	Par 5	18	460	Par 4
In	3308	Par 36	In	3456	Par 36

HOTEL INFORMATION

Carden Park Hotel, Golf Resort & Spa
Chester, Cheshire
England CH3 9DQ
Tel: 01829 731000
Fax: 01829 731032
Rating: 4 Star AA & RAC, Relais Du Golf.

Rooms: 192.
Restaurants: The Seventeenth – Fine dining: The Garden Restaurant – A la Carte: Brasserie Renard – informal: The Clubhouse.
Hair and Beauty: Ladies hair dressing salon + extensive spa.
Fitness Facilities: 20 metre pool, saunas, steam rooms, wet & dry relaxation areas, 15 treatment rooms, dance studio and gym.
Other Sporting Facilities: Tennis, mountain biking, extensive walks.

TARIFF

Golf Breaks:
Dinner, B&B + 18 holes on Cheshire Course from £75.00.
Dinner, B&B + 18 holes on Nicklaus Course from £95.00.
Dinner, B&B + 18 holes on Nicklaus Course + 18 holes on Cheshire Course from £115.00.

Leisure Breaks:
Dinner , bed & breakfast from £55.00

Prices quoted are per person per night, based on two sharing, and include complimentary use of the leisure facilities.

Upgrades to suites at additional cost, subject to availability.

Visit www.cardenpark.co.ok for details of special offers

DIRECTIONS

From the South: take the M6 to junction 10a joining the M54, Then take junction 3 off the M54 onto the A41. Stay on the A41 Chester for approx. 35 minutes. Turn left at the Broxton roundabout onto the A534 Wrexham. Continue along the A534 for approx. 1.5 miles, Carden park entrance is on the left.

From the North: take the M6 junction 20 signposted M56 North Wales/Runcorn, then take junction 15 off the M56 for M53 Chester. Take the A41 junction for Whitchurch, staying on the A41 for approx. 8 miles. At the Broxton roundabout turn right onto the A534 Wrexham continuing for approx. 1.5 miles, Carden Park entrance is on left.

Hawkstone Park Hotel

*H*awkstone Park is known as the 'Jewel of Shropshire' and is able to provide the perfect location for all your golfing needs. The facility is set in 400 acres of idyllic parkland, which offers the peace and tranquillity of the Shropshire countryside within a few miles of the motorway networks.

LOCAL ATTRACTIONS

Local attractions include Ironbridge, the historic towns of Shrewsbury, Chester and Nantwich. Clay shooting, archery, croquet and hot-air ballooning are available with prior notification.

The hotel is bounded on all sides by two 18 hole championship courses. Supporting these is a 6 hole par 3, academy course, a driving range, practice area and a purpose built golf centre incorporating a well stocked golf shop. We have high class changing rooms and Golf Professional Services offering teaching facilities for the beginner and improver. The top floor Terrace Room offers all day bar and restaurant facilities with wonderful, panoramic views over the courses. The hotel's 65 en-suite bedrooms, all newly refurbished have tea and coffee making facilities, radio and satellite T.V., trouser press, iron and hairdryer. The elegant restaurant which overlooks the landscaped gardens offers a high standard of traditional British and classical French cuisine. There is a large, comfortable snooker room with two tables and a card room and private bar and variety of comprehensively equipped meeting and conference rooms. Hawkstone Historic Park and Follies complements the hotel and golf courses where Sandy Lyle learned his game.

GOLF INFORMATION

2 x18 holes parkland courses.
Hawkstone 6491yards. Windmill 6476 yards.
Par 72/72

Golf Professional: Paul Wesselingh

Practice facilities: Academy 6 hole, Par 3 course,
Practice range and putting greens.

Instructions: Groups and individuals catered for.

Hire: Clubs trollies and buggies.

Green Fees: Mon-Fri from £16.00 – Sat-Sun from £22.00.
Day Society Packages from £20.95 per person

Purpose built Golf Centre, Golf Shop, 5 Star changing rooms, Terrace
Bar & Restaurant with balcony open all day overlooking 12th Century
Castle. All golfers are advised to reserve tee time in advance to avoid
disappointment and must register at the Golf Centre at least 20
minutes prior to play to collect golf ticket.

CARD OF THE COURSE
Hawkstone

1	374	Par 4	10	517	Par 5
2	402	Par 4	11	438	Par 4
3	216	Par 3	12	145	Par 3
4	332	Par 4	13	373	Par 4
5	371	Par 4	14	485	Par 5
6	364	Par 4	15	315	Par 4
7	434	Par 4	16	256	Par 4
8	481	Par 5	17	383	Par 4
9	188	Par 3	18	417	Par 4
Out	3162	Par 35	In	3329	Par 37

HOTEL INFORMATION

Weston-under-Redcastle,
Shrewsbury, Shropshire, SY4
5UY
Tel: 01939 200611
Fax: 01939 200311

Rating: ETC 3 Star Silver.

Rooms: 65 en suite with tea & coffee
making facilities, satellite TV, direct dial
telephone, hairdryer, trouser press and
iron.

Restaurants: Hawkstone restaurant –
formal, classic French with traditional
British food.

TARIFF

Rooms from £75.00 per
person per night.

Breakfast, full English
£8.50 - Continental
£4.95.

Residential Special Golf Packages:
From £52.00 per person per night,
dinner B&B + one round of golf.
based on two people sharing a
twin/double.

DIRECTIONS

Located in North
Shropshire between
Shrewsbury and
Whitchurch off the A49,
easily accessible from the
M6 and M54. Follow the
brown and white signs into the
village of Weston-under-Redcastle.

SHROPSHIRE

Hill Valley Golf & Country Club

*H*ill Valley is home to two magnificent Golf Courses. The Emerald Championship layout was designed nearly 30 years ago by the TV and golfing stars Peter Alliss and Dave Thomas. The shorter, but no less challenging, Sapphire course has matured into a stern test of the short game. Peter Alliss did oversee the

construction of the Sapphire Course without actually laying down the fundamental designs.

The attractive and well shaped fairways, highlighting the very best of rural Shropshire, thread their challenging way through 300 exciting acres of trees, lakes and picturesque streams to American style greens defended by sand and water.

Hill Valley's mature Championship Emerald Course has been home successively to world international stars, Ian Woosnam, Jonathan Lomas and Michael Welch. Additionally, Ryder Cup players such as John O'Leary and John Garner have been associated with the club in the past.

The hotel has 28 on-course bedrooms, all en-suite and can offer a 70 seat luxury à la carte restaurant and a conference suite with a capacity of 200 for business meetings and social functions. A separate bar and breakfast room is located in the conference suite area. Also situated in the complex is the Leisure Suite comprising a gym, jacuzzi, sunbed, sauna, steam room and snooker table.

GOLF INFORMATION

Emerald 18 hole and Sapphire 18 hole, 6628 and 4801 yards, parkland with American trapped and holding greens. Par 73 & 66.

Golf Professional: Clive Burgess
Tel: 01948 663032

Practice facilities: Driving range.

Instructions: Groups and individuals catered for.

Hire: Clubs and buggies

CARD OF THE COURSE

Sapphire Course			Emerald Course		
1	388	Par 4	1	471	Par 5
2	157	Par 3	2	405	Par 4
3	360	Par 4	3	411	Par 4
4	123	Par 3	4	196	Par 3
5	326	Par 4	5	524	Par 5
6	166	Par 3	6	187	Par 3
7	314	Par 4	7	501	Par 5
8	149	Par 3	8	434	Par 4
9	323	Par 4	9	370	Par 4
Out	2306	Par 32	Out	3499	Par 37
10	104	Par 3	1	392	Par 4
11	288	Par 4	2	390	Par 4
12	301	Par 4	3	355	Par 4
13	190	Par 3	4	477	Par 5
14	308	Par 4	5	357	Par 4
15	477	Par 5	6	178	Par 3
16	310	Par 4	7	490	Par 5
17	169	Par 3	8	175	Par 3
18	348	Par 4	9	315	Par 4
In	2495	Par 34	Out	3129	Par 36

HOTEL INFORMATION

Hill Valley Golf & Country Club
Terrick Road, Whitchurch
Shropshire SY13 4JZ
Tel: 01948 663584
Fax: 01948 665927
email: info@hill-valley.co.uk
www: www.hill-valley.co.uk

Rooms: 28.
Restaurants: A La Carte + Society Room
Childcare: By arrangement
Hair and Beauty: By arrangement – Mobile visitor.
Fitness Facilities: Gym, Sauna, Steam room, Jacuzzi, sun bed.
Other Sporting Facilities: Snooker, shooting, fishing and horse racing nearby.
Other Leisure Activities: Cabaret Nights, shopping trips to Chester, Chauffered Rolls Royce.

TARIFF

Dinner + B&B + Golf from £40 per person per day.

Society Packages from £17.50 per person.

Personalised Packages:
To meet all requirements.
Corporate days and business arranged as required.

DIRECTIONS

With its excellent road, rail and airport links, Hill Valley is easily accessible from anywhere in the UK or abroad. Manchester International airport – 1 hour. Crewe (railway station) – 30 mins. Chester & Shrewsbury are just 30 mins down the road.

Directly off Whitchurch ring road A41/A49 well signposted 1 mile north of Whitchurch.

Hilton Puckrup Hall

*T*his former Regency Manor House set in 160 acres of parkland has been sympathetically extended into a luxury 112 bedroomed hotel offering extensive conference and banqueting facilities, full Livingwell health and leisure club comprising swimming pool, superb gymnasium, saunas, steam room and beauty treatment room.

LOCAL ATTRACTIONS

Set between the Cotswolds and The Malverns, the hotel is just 12 miles equidistant between Worcester with its famous cathedrals, Royal Worcester China Factory and cricket ground and Cheltenham with beautiful shops and famous racecourse. Stratford-on-Avon is less than an hour away, Eastnor Castle is within half an hour and the Malvern Hills, within sight of the hotel, are a 20 minute drive across country.

Balharries Restaurant offers a TOH and à la carte menu in a continental atmosphere, whilst private dining is available in any of our 16 function rooms or 2 ballrooms for up to 180 people.

The golf course opened in 1992 and was recently re-designed to provide an excellent practice area. Tipped 'Out of the Top Drawer' in Golf Monthly May 1996, the 6189 yard par 70 course is set in mature parkland and provides a test of golf for both the novice and experienced golfer alike.

The Par 5 fifth hole measuring 531 yards requires two long and accurate shots to set up a birdie opportunity. There are three lakes and bunkers to manoeuvre the ball over and around, with superb views of the Malvern Hills.

Strategic bunkering and fairway sculpturing around dog-legs set up a fine back nine, culminating in the magnificent 18th hole. Measuring 200 yards over water with the Hotel as a backdrop, it's a finishing hole of top quality. The grounds also hold a dedicated area for clay pigeon shooting, archery and buggy driving.

18 hole, 6189 yard parkland course

Par 70

Golf Professional: Kevin Pickett
Tel: 01684 271591

Instructions: Groups and individuals catered for.

Hire: Buggies, Trolleys.

CARD OF THE COURSE

1	337	Par 4	10	319	Par 4
2	126	Par 3	11	185	Par 3
3	486	Par 4	12	457	Par 4
4	338	Par 4	13	475	Par 5
5	531	Par 5	14	559	Par 5
6	332	Par 4	15	389	Par 4
7	160	Par 3	16	184	Par 3
8	320	Par 4	17	345	Par 4
9	446	Par 4	18	200	Par 3
Out 3076 Par 35			In 3113 Par 35		

Hilton Puckrup Hall
Puckrup
Tewkesbury
Gloucestershire GL20 6GL
Tel: 01684 296200
Fax: 01684 850788
Rooms: 112.
Restaurants: 1–Balharries – English a
la Carte and TOH.
Childcare Facilities: None offered – Private
arrangements can be made.
Hair and Beauty: Beauty facilities on site, hair
can be arranged.
Fitness Facilities: Gymnasium, swimming pool,
saunas, steam room, fitness assessment room.
Other Sporting Facilities: Buggy driving, archery,
clay pigeon shooting available by arrangement for
parties over 20 people.
Other Leisure Activities: Murder mystery
weekends, wine weekends.

£115 Single occupancy of
Double room.
£130 Double room
£150 Suites and four
posters.

Special Golf Packages:
Breaks from £82.50 B&Bpp + Golf for
2 nights sharing double or twin room.

Other Special Golf Packages:
£92.50 DB&Bpp + Golf, 2 nights,
sharing double or twin.

M50 junction 1 - take
A38 towards Tewkesbury,
hotel and golf club is 200
yards along this road on
the right hand side.

Nailcote Hall Hotel

*N*ailcote Hall is a delightful 17th century country house set in 15 acres of parkland, ideally located just 10 minutes drive from Birmingham International Airport, the NEC and at the heart of the Midland's motorway network.

Small may be beautiful but in the case of the par 3 at Nailcote Hall, it can be very tough too.

Nailcote Hall is the host to the 'British Professional Short Championship' each year, making this an annual event in the golf calendar when a number of European Tour players pit their wits against each other. The 9 hole Cromwell course has been specially designed to provide even experienced golfers with a tough test of their short game. All the hazards of a full scale course, ditches, water and 23 bunkers, not to mention the elevated greens, are here, with just that 1st big drive missing. Sid Mouland, 6 times Welsh Champion and World Cup player is the resident golf professional and is available to give either individual or group tuition and is the tournament director for all of Nailcote's golfing events. Famous golf courses within easy driving of Nailcote Hall include; The Belfry, The Forest of Arden and The Warwickshire. For dining, Nailcote offers the traditional style of the award winning Oak Room restaurant or the Mediterranean atmosphere of 'Rick's Bar' which provides a regular programme of live entertainment, combine all of this with 38 luxury bedrooms, superb leisure complex and tennis courts to make Nailcote a 'Venue for all Reasons'.

GOLF INFORMATION

9 hole Championship Short Course, 1031 yard parkland course

Par 27

Golf Professional: Sid Mouland

Tel: 024 7646 6174
www.nailcotehall.co.uk
email: golf@nailcotehall.co.uk

Instructions: Groups and individuals catered for. Resident Professional

Hire: Clubs

Green Fees: £10.00 pp 18 holes.

CARD OF THE COURSE		
1	116	Par 3
2	114	Par 3
3	124	Par 3
4	87	Par 3
5	95	Par 3
6	110	Par 3
7	146	Par 3
8	106	Par 3
9	133	Par 3
Total	1023	Par 27

HOTEL INFORMATION

Nailcote Hall Hotel
Nailcote Lane
Berkswell
Warwickshire CV7 7DE

Tel: 024 7646 6174
Fax: 024 7646 0720

Rooms: 38.

Restaurants: Oak Room – Traditional oak beamed - Modern International cuisine – Rick's bar – Mediterranean Style Bistro.

Hair and Beauty: Kanebo Facial, body, hand nail and feet treatments, waxing and make-up.

Fitness Facilities: 14 metre roman style swimming pool, steam room, gym, jacuzzi, beauty salon championship 9 hole par 27 golf course, croquet, 2 all weather tennis courts.

Other Leisure Activities: Murder Mystery weekends, live musical entertainment regular programme, laser/clay shooting can be arranged (for groups).

TARIFF

Special Golf Packages:
2 nights DBB £189p.p. including green fees for Stoneleigh Deer Park Golf Club. Overnight golf break at Nailcote Hall £140 per room + £10.00 green fee per person.

Other Special Golf Packages:
Health & Beauty Breaks from £135.00 per night + "Away for a Day" breaks from £69 to £98.00.

DIRECTIONS

Nailcote Hall is situated on the B4101 Balsall Common/Coventry Road within 10 minutes of Birmingham International Airport/Station.

North Shore Hotel & Golf Course

*T*he North Shore Hotel, built in 1910, is a privately owned hotel and golf course situated within its own extensive grounds on the quiet fringes of Skegness, only a five minute walk from the centre, or a step away from the sea.

The golf course, one of the main attractions at the North Shore, was designed and built in 1910 by the legendary James Braid. He took advantage of the many undulations in the ground and constructed a fine three-tier, eighteen hole course, split into two distinct halves. A peaceful and calm drift from the Links, facing the sea, to a mature Parkland course. Although the course will test every area of your game, the expansive fairways are forgiving to the higher handicap player.

The hotel boasts 36 bedrooms, all with en-suite facilities, a fine oak panelled restaurant offers the finest in cuisine and hospitality. Overlooking the rolling fairways and sea and offering an extensive quality bar menu is the James Braid Bar with a full range of premium lagers and real ales, all of which are served throughout the day. The Pro Shop, public bars, restaurant and separate games room and function room are available to both members and residents alike.

The North Shore prides itself on offering excellent service with friendly staff and has been established as one of the top venues in Lincolnshire and the east coast for society days, corporate hospitality, society group bookings, golfing breaks and holidays.

LOCAL ATTRACTIONS

Less than a mile away is Skegness with beach walks, the Promenade, amusement rides, Skegness pier, with ten-pin bowling and Laserquest, horse rides along the beach as well as an abundant area of unspoilt East Lincolnshire countryside.

The historic city of Lincoln is within easy driving distance.

GOLF INFORMATION

18 hole, 6257 yard half links, half parkland

Par 71

Golf Professional: John Cornelius

Tel: 01754 764822

Instructions: Groups and individuals catered for.

Hire: Clubs

CARD OF THE COURSE

1	503	Par 5	10	410	Par 4
2	418	Par 4	11	157	Par 3
3	186	Par 3	12	309	Par 4
4	373	Par 4	13	358	Par 4
5	472	Par 4	14	141	Par 3
6	267	Par 4	15	429	Par 4
7	499	Par 5	16	417	Par 4
8	399	Par 4	17	349	Par 4
9	251	Par 4	18	319	Par 4
Out	3368	Par 37	In	2889	Par 34

HOTEL INFORMATION

The North Shore Hotel and Golf Course
North Shore Road, Skegness, Lincolnshire PE25 1DN
Tel: 01754 763298
Fax: 01754 761902

Rating: RAC 3 Star, ETB Welcome Host.
Rooms: 36.
Restaurants: All day home cooked bar food, plus restaurant serving traditional English food.
Childcare Facilities: Baby listening through switch board.
Other Leisure Activities: Easter weekend, Valentines weekend, Christmas weekend, September open competition week.

TARIFF

B&B from £32.00 per person per night.
DB&B from £42.00 weekdays, £47.50 weekends.

Special Golf Packages:
B&B including 18 holes Midweek £51.00, Weekend £71.00.

Other Special Golf Packages:
Winter x 2 nights + 3 rounds golf £95.00
Summer x 2 nights + 4 rounds golf from £161.00

DIRECTIONS

When approaching on the A158 turn left onto Roman Bank at the traffic lights (Ship Inn) and follow the road for ½ mile. Turn right just after the pelican crossing onto North Shore Road. The hotel is situated on the left, at the end of the road.

When approaching on the A52 from Boston, follow the one way system onto Roman Bank signed 'Mablethorpe' and Ingoldmelds and continue past the traffic lights (Ship Inn) and follow road for ½ mile. Turn right just after the pelican crossing onto North Shore Road, the hotel is situated on the left, at the end of the road.

St David's Park Hotel

*A*t St David's Park Hotel, we endeavour to provide every leisure need and business facility that today's guest expects.

The Hotel is situated at the great crossroads of North Wales, where the A55 meets the A494 and is just 10 minutes drive from the M56.

We have 145 bedrooms and suites where luxury and comfort surround the guests. There are a number of excutive ladies rooms, non-smoking rooms and specially designed rooms for disabled guests.

We are especially well equipped to satisfy your business needs and are well known for providing conference facilities and an expertly trained team of staff who really care.

In the Fountains Restaurant an international à la carte menu and a less formal carvery are served. The more relaxed Club Cafe, situated within the Health Club offers a wide selection of drinks, pastries and snacks plus its daily 'Plat du Jour' menu.

Our nearby Northop Country Park Golf Club has the superb colonially inspired 'Far Pavilions' resaurant. Enjoy its extensive à la carte and 'Greenside' menu, whilst taking in the magnificent views of the 18th Green.

With its fabulous setting of mature woodland and parkland, it is one of the finist, and has numerous touraments including the Welsh PGA Championship.

The course was designed by former British Ryder Cupo Captain, John Jacobs, to be a real test for golfers of all abilities. In addition to the challenging 18 holes, there's also tennis and a fully equipped gymnasium.

The fully equipped Heath Club at St David's Park Hotel is just about as comprehensive as oyu could possibly wish.

LOCAL ATTRACTIONS

Explore and visit some of Britain's most interesting places or shop till you drop! The historic City of Chester, the breathtaking scenic splendour of snowdonia National Park and the golden coast of North Wales are all nearby. Liverpool's famous Albert Dock with its attractions and the recently opened Trafford Centre in Manchester are also within easy driving distance.

GOLF INFORMATION

18 hole, 6735 yard parkland course

Par 72

Golf Professional: Mathew Pritchard

Practice facilities: Driving Range, 2 Putting Greens, 1 Chipping Green.

Instructions: from £15.00

Hire: Clubs £10.00, Trolleys £1.50, Buggies £15.00

Northop Country Park is Located 2 miles from St. David's Park

CARD OF THE COURSE

1	541	Par 5	10	354	Par 4
2	180	Par 3	11	559	Par 5
3	441	Par 4	12	349	Par 4
4	355	Par 4	13	349	Par 4
5	203	Par 3	14	192	Par 3
6	393	Par 4	15	522	Par 5
7	428	Par 4	16	378	Par 4
8	505	Par 5	17	156	Par 3
9	390	Par 4	18	440	Par 4
Out	3436	Par 36	In	3299	Par 36

HOTEL INFORMATION

St David's Park Hotel Golf Club
St David's Park, Ewloe, Near Chester,
Flintshire. CH5 3YB.
Tel: +44 (0) 1244 520800
Fax: +44 (0) 1244 520930
Rating: AA/RAC 4 Star Hotel.
Rooms: 145

Restaurants: Fountains Club Café
Childcare Facilities: Dai the Den, Childrens purpose built playroom.
Hair and Beauty: Beauty 2 Beauty rooms.
Fitness Facilities: Health Club swimming pool, snooker/pool room, whirl pool, sauna/steam room and solarium.

TARIFF

**Single/Double /Twin £109.00
Studio Suites £130.00
Morgan Suite £154.00**

Leisure Breaks:
from £72.00.
Golfing Breaks:
from £87.00 per person sharing twin/double, one round of golf, dinner B&B.

DIRECTIONS

From M6 Junction 20: Signposted M56 - North Wales/Runcorn/Birkenhead Follow M56 junction 15 for M53 Chester. Follow A55 North Wales for 12 miles. Careful at A55/A494 junction, follow A494 Queensferry junction, Not A55, St David's Park is signposted just past the Queensferry junction, then take the left slip-road B5127, Buckley.

Telford Golf & Country Club

The Telford Golf and Country Club overlooks the beauty of the Ironbridge Gorge. Standing on the Iron Bridge itself, beneath you is Britain's longest river, The Severn, and on either side woodlands that cover the steep sides of the valley.

To explore this wonderful scenery there is no better base than Telford Golf and Country

LOCAL ATTRACTIONS

The Iron Bridge, nine fascinating museums in Ironbridge, antiques warehouse two miles, RAF Cosford museum, Telford Shopping Centre with its wonderful lakes and gardens, vineyard, Roman remains, home of the Gingerbread Man, - for places to visit you're spoiled for choice.

Club, warm and welcoming in it's ambience and renowned for it's comfort and cuisine. The facilities include 2 Restaurants and Bars, extensive private dining facilities, and a Leisure Suite which includes an 14 x 9 metre indoor heated swimming pool, gymnasium, sauna, jacuzzi, solarium and squash courts.

If you are a keen golfer you can test your skills on our own 18 hole Championship Golf Course. The picturesque course offers a number of challenging holes and boasts greens designed and laid using the 'suspended water table' system. Used at Augusta National Golf Club in Georgia, home of the US Masters, we are confident that this system has produced putting surfaces which are among the best that you will ever experience.

Before your game you can browse around our Golf Shop and warm up using the extensive practice facilities. Our own Full Time Teaching Professional offers a variety of coaching styles, appropriate to every standard of golfer.

Overall, Telford Golf And Country Club offers the 'complete package', whether the purpose of your visit is a golf or leisure break.

GOLF INFORMATION

18 hole, 6761 yard parkland course Par 72

Golf Professional: Dan Bateman
Tel: 01952 586052

Practice facilities: Driving Range, practice bunker, putting green, chipping green.

Instructions: Groups and individuals catered for.

Hire: Clubs and buggies.

CARD OF THE COURSE

1	399	Par 4	10	399	Par 4
2	498	Par 5	11	170	Par 3
3	165	Par 3	12	402	Par 4
4	391	Par 4	13	517	Par 5
5	408	Par 4	14	440	Par 4
6	534	Par 5	15	313	Par 4
7	195	Par 3	16	191	Par 3
8	385	Par 4	17	529	Par 5
9	430	Par 4	18	395	Par 4
Out	3405	Par 36	In	3356	Par 36

HOTEL INFORMATION

Telford Golf & Country Club
Great Hay Drive, Sutton Heights,
Telford. TF7 4DT
Tel: 01952 429977
Fax: 01952 586602
Rating: AA 3 Star.
Rooms: 96.
Restaurants: Brasserie Restaurant, Cafe bar - both modern.
Childcare Facilities: Listening.
Beauty Facilities: Beauty & masseur
Fitness Facilities: Gym Jacuzzi, sunbed, heated pool, steam room, sauna, squash courts, snooker tables.

Othe Sporting Facilities: On site 'Corporate' event activities on request eg laser clays, 4x4 driving.

Other Leisure Activities: Various 'Cabaret' events during year - various dates.

TARIFF

B&B + 18 holes
£94.75 + £20.00.

Other Special Golf Packages
2 night dinner bed & breakfast + golf from £69.50 per person per night.

Weekend Breaks
£85.00 room only. £59.50 DBB Break.
£6950 golf DBB Break.
Breaks over 2 nts single supps apply.

DIRECTIONS

M54 Junction 4.
A442 Kidderminster follow 'Brown' tourist signs for Telford GolfClub.

Tewkesbury Park Hotel & Golf Club

*H*igh above Tewkesbury, an historic, Abbey town, Tewksbury Park Hotel has wonderful views across the Gloucestershire countryside, to the Severn Valley and Malvern Hills. It's a truly idyllic setting for this extended 18th century manor house.

Set in 176 acres of parkland, the Frank Pennick designed course provides a variety of challenges from wooded areas to water hazards, with spacious fairways opening up as the round progresses.

The five par 5's, all over 500 yards do offer Birdie opportunities. The 431 yard fourth is a testing par 4 with a long up hill approach. The fifth is a very attractive par 3, over a lake to a raised green.

There are covered bays on the practice ground, which includes a driving range with targets and distance markers.

Additional facilities include professional tuition from our fully equipped golf shop, which also offers trolley, buggy, club hire and video facilities.

The hotel has 78 comfortable, ensuite bedrooms, the majority with panoramic views across the parkland course. All rooms are complete with tea/coffee making facilities, trouser-press, telephone and television, including Sky. The Leisure Club, complimentary to Golfing Breaks guests, has an indoor pool, squash and tennis courts, sauna, spa and gym. Beauty treatments in the salon are bookable in advance.

Good food and wines are offered in Tewkesbury Park Hotel's two restaurants, and the '19th' bar with its attractive terrace, has direct access from the 18th hole: the perfect setting to sit and watch the sun go down over the hills. Private dining for prize-givings, parties or other events can easily be arranged in our Marquee or in one of the suites (accommodating up to 180!). The hotel staff are friendly and helpful, adding to the informal and hospitable atmosphere of this lovely hotel.

LOCAL ATTRACTIONS

The oldest medieval town in England, Tewksbury is an absolute delight with its black & white timbered buildings and famous alleyways. the Abbey was built in 1090 and must be seen! Running alongside Tewkesbury are the rivers Severn and Avon, adding to the beauty and uniqueness of this little-known town. The Malvern Hills are a short car ride, as are the Cotswold villages, Stratford-upon-Avon and elegant, Regency Cheltenham (with its racecourse famous for the Murphy's Golf Cup).

GOLF INFORMATION

**18 hole, 6533 yard parkland course
Par 73**

Golf Professional: Robert Taylor
Tel: 01684 294892

Practice facilities: Covered driving range.

Instructions: Groups and individuals catered for + Swing Analysis.

Hire: Clubs and buggies

CARD OF THE COURSE					
1	519	Par 5	10	200	Par 3
2	321	Par 4	11	422	Par 4
3	503	Par 5	12	517	Par 5
4	431	Par 4	13	416	Par 4
5	146	Par 3	14	339	Par 4
6	575	Par 5	15	501	Par 5
7	128	Par 3	16	178	Par 3
8	349	Par 4	17	371	Par 4
9	352	Par 4	18	265	Par 4
Out	3324	Par 37	In	3209	Par 36

HOTEL INFORMATION

Tewkesbury Park Hotel & Golf Club
Lincoln Green Lane
Tewkesbury
Gloucestershire GL20 7DN
Tel: 01684 295405
Fax: 01684 292386
Rating: 3 Star AA+RAC – 4 Crowns ETB.
Rooms: 78.
Restaurants: Garden Restaurant – Table d'hôte and à la carte. Pavilion Restaurant – Light lunches and snacks.
Childcare Facilities: Baby Listening – Free. Babysitters creche can be arranged.
Health and Beauty: Salon on site offering all facilities e.g. massages, facials, waxing etc.
Fitness Facilities: *Complimentary:* indoor heated swimming pool, fully equipped gymnasium, fitness centre, jacuzzi, sauna and solarium.
Other Sporting Facilities: *Complimentary:* 6 hole par 3 course, tennis courts, squash courts and 10 acre activity field.
Other Leisure Activities: All themed events can be organised for private parties – details on request.

TARIFF

Dinner Bed and Breakfast and golf from £59 per person based on 2 people sharing a twin or double room for a minimum of 2 nights stay.

Other Special Golf Packages:

As advertised in local and national golfing publications.

DIRECTIONS

Leave the M5 at Junction 9 or the M50 at Junction 1. Follow the signs into Tewkesbury Town Centre, go over the roundabout and follow signs to Tewkesbury Abbey. The Abbey will appear on your left and Lincoln Green Lane is approximately 500 yards past the Abbey on your right, immediately before the Esso Garage. The Hotel is at the end of Lincoln Green Lane.

Thornbury Golf Lodge

*T*he Old Farmhouse exterior of Thornbury Golf Lodge disguises a completely refurbished interior with 11 elegant and comfortable bedrooms, most of which afford stunning views over the Severn Estuary and our two courses.

The bedrooms are spacious and individually designed with traditional furniture and

LOCAL ATTRACTIONS

The Lodge is perfect for visiting golfers or simply as a touring holiday base. Bristol is only 10 miles away and the City of Bath, the Cotswolds and the Wye Valley are within easy reach.

An ideal base for the duration of the Badminton or Gatcombe Park Horse Trials combined with a visit to view the exterior of Highgrove House.

The magnificent Slimbridge Wildfowl Trust is less that 20 minutes away.

Those who enjoy shopping will find something to cater for all their needs at "The Mall" the recently opened out of town Regional Shopping Centre.

fittings, all with ensuite bath or shower. Tea and coffee making facilities, satellite TV and direct dial telephones are provided in every room.

Meals are available in the Clubhouse, where there is a snack bar, restaurant and well-stocked bar, all served in welcoming, informal surroundings.

There are two 18 hole courses, one of which is a Par 3. In addition there is a 25 bay floodlit range complete with video tuition bay. Golf lessons with the resident PGA qualified professional can be arranged in either group or individual format. The comprehensive golf shop carries a full range of equipment and clothing, together with club and trolley hire.

Conference facilities are also available, enabling you to combine business with pleasure. We will be delighted to provide a competitive personal quotation based upon a tailor-made programme designed specifically for your needs.

GOLF INFORMATION

**18 hole, 6154 yard parkland course
Par 71**

Golf Professional: Simon Hubbard
Tel: 01454 281155

Practice facilities: Covered driving range.

Instructions: Groups and individuals catered for +
Video tuition.

Hire: Clubs

CARD OF THE COURSE					
1	508	Par 5	10	394	Par 4
2	148	Par 3	11	303	Par 4
3	356	Par 4	12	135	Par 3
4	359	Par 4	13	444	Par 4
5	337	Par 4	14	158	Par 3
6	145	Par 3	15	480	Par 5
7	308	Par 4	16	327	Par 4
8	394	Par 4	17	386	Par 4
9	451	Par 4	18	521	Par 5
Out 3006		Par 35	In 3148		Par 36

GLOUSTERSHIRE

HOTEL INFORMATION

Thornbury Golf Lodge
Thornbury Golf Centre
Bristol Road
Thornbury
South Gloustershire

Tel: 01454 281144
Fax: 01454 281177

Rooms: 11.

Restaurants: English Food

Other Sporting Facilities: Leisure Centre
half a mile from lodge.

TARIFF

B&B Dinner one night
including 18 holes of golf
from £50 per person per
night.

Special Golf Packages:
Tailor made packages on request.

DIRECTIONS

At Junction 16 of M5
head north on A38 for 5
miles - at traffic lights
adjacent to Rover main
dealer (Berkeley Vale
Motors) turn left towards
Thornbury. One mile downhill
opposite Leisure Centre the
entrance to the Golf Club is on
the left.

Welcombe Hotel and Golf Course

LOCAL ATTRACTIONS

- Royal Shakespeare Theatre

- Warwick Castle

- Blenheim Palace

- Cotswold Villages

- Shakespeare Tour

*E*njoying a reputation for its exceptional service and comfort, fine cuisine, traditional English country house ambience and an incomparable parkland setting, the Welcombe Hotel and Golf Course has long been the natural choice of those who appreciate the very best.

Set in 157 acres with a beautifully manicured championship golf course of undulating parkland with its wealth of mature trees and lakes, once owned by William Shakespeare, this Jacobean style mansion house hotel remains one of the jewels of the Heart of England. With a combination of luxurious accommodation in the form of 64 bedrooms, fine conference facilities, a health and beauty suite and award winning cuisine the Welcombe boasts every facility for business and pleasure.

New Clubhouse opening Spring 2000.

GOLF INFORMATION

18 hole, 6288 yard parkland course

Par 70

Director of Golf: Carl Mason
Tel: 01789 295252

Corporate Golf Office: 01789 262665

Practice facilities: Outdoor driving range.

Instructions: Groups and individuals catered for.

Hire: Clubs, buggies and trollies.

Green Fees: £40 midweek, £50 weekends.

Company Golf Days welcome, prices upon application.

CARD OF THE COURSE

1	477	Par 5	10	380	Par 4
2	174	Par 3	11	201	Par 3
3	454	Par 4	12	373	Par 4
4	390	Par 4	13	390	Par 4
5	312	Par 4	14	173	Par 3
6	181	Par 3	15	402	Par 4
7	362	Par 4	16	521	Par 5
8	407	Par 4	17	400	Par 4
9	186	Par 3	18	505	Par 5
Out	2943	Par 34	In	3345	Par 36

HOTEL INFORMATION

Welcombe Hotel and
Golf Course
Warwick Road,
Stratford-upon-Avon
Warwickshire CV37 0NR
Tel: 01789 295252
Fax: 01789 414666

Rating: 4 Star & 2 AA Rosettes for cuisine.
Rooms: 64.
Restaurants: Trevelyan Restaurant (Award winning) French/English
Childcare Facilities: Babysitting available.
Hair and Beauty: Hair, Health & Beauty salon on site.
Fitness Facilities: Small multi-gym.
Other Sporting Facilities: 18 hole golf course, tennis courts (all weather + floodlit).

TARIFF

2 Day Golf Break including dinner, bed & breakfast + 2 rounds of golf **£250** per person. Accommodation from **£105+vat** per room single occupancy, B&B.

Special Golf Packages:
No packages – All arrangements tailored to suit.

DIRECTIONS

Situated on the main Warwick to Stratford-upon-Avon A439, 1 mile from Stratford Town Centre.

From M40, exit at Junction 15, Warwick, taking the A46 then A439 to Stratford-upon-Avon.

Whitefields Hotel, Golf & Country Club

Situated in the heart of the Warwickshire countryside, Whitefields Hotel, Golf and Country Club is an ideal base for visitors to the Heart of England. Close to the M1, M45, M6, The National Exhibition Centre, The National Agricultural Centre and both Birmingham and Coventry airports it is an ideal venue for business meetings, conferences and corporate hospitality days.

The 18-hole course overlooks the beautiful Draycote Water where water sports and country pursuits are available to visitors. A recently-opened 16-bay driving range offers state-of-the-art facilities.
Golf clubs and societies are particularly welcome.

Our deluxe rooms provide a high standard of comfort for our guests. A total of 50 rooms, 25 with bath and shower en-suite, 25 with shower en-suite, have colour TV, telephone and tea and coffee making facilities. One bedroom has been adapted for disabled guests. All rooms are non smoking.

You can enjoy fine dining and excellent wines in the Garden Restaurant or choose the more informal atmosphere of the Draycote Bar or Spikes Bar.

LOCAL ATTRACTIONS

The National Exhibition Centre, National Agricultural Centre, Stratford-on-Avon, Warwick Castle, Coventry Cathedral and Rugby School are within easy driving distance. Car hire is available from the hotel.

Water sports, country pursuits, wind surfing and trout fishing are all within easy reach.

GOLF INFORMATION

18 hole, 6223 yard course
Par 71
Practice facilities: Covered driving range.
   Instructions: Groups and individuals catered for. 18 hole putting green.
Hire: Clubs and buggies.
Green fees: April 1 to November 31.
Visitors: Monday to Friday **£18** a round **£25** per day. Weekends and Bank Holidays **£22** a round **£30** per day.

CARD OF THE COURSE					
1	361	Par 4	10	188	Par 3
2	349	Par 4	11	351	Par 4
3	318	Par 4	12	329	Par 4
4	359	Par 4	13	435	Par 4
5	194	Par 3	14	483	Par 5
6	448	Par 4	15	251	Par 4
7	450	Par 4	16	174	Par 3
8	476	Par 5	17	314	Par 4
9	359	Par 4	18	384	Par 4
Out	3314	Par 36	In	2909	Par 35

HOTEL INFORMATION

Whitefields Hotel Golf & Country Club
Coventry Road,
Thurlaston, Rugby,
Warwickshire CV23 9JR
Tel: 01788 521800/815555
Fax: 01788 521695
Rating: AA 3 Star.
Rooms: 50.
Restaurants: Serves a la carte – table de hote or bar snacks daily.

TARIFF

Special Golf Packages:
Summer Breaks –(April 1999 to November 1999):
SOCIETY DAY GOLD
(with accommodation);
Bed, Breakfast, Evening Three Course Dinner and Golf £74.50, based on two sharing a room. £15 Single Room Supplement.
SOCIETY DAY SILVER: £39.50
SOCIETY DAY BRONZE: £29.50
Winter Breaks – Please telephone for packages available.

DIRECTIONS

Whitefields can be located on the A45 between Rugby and Coventry. Birmingham Airport is close by. M1 on to the M45 will take you straight onto the A45.

BELLS HOTEL & THE FOREST OF DEAN GOLF CLUB

Lords Hill, Coleford, Glos. GL16 8BE   Tel: 01594 832583 Fax: 01594 832584 e-mail:
enquiries@bells-hotel.co.uk

18 HOLES PAR 70 6033 YARDS
TYPE OF GOLF COURSE: Parkland
GOLF PROFESSIONAL: John Hansel
TEL: 01594 833689

B&B + 18 HOLES: From £40.00pppn
half Board from £57.00pppn (includes
complimentary Golf)

Weekend Breaks from £65.00pppn including
complimentary Golf & Sunday Lunch.
Conference & Golf Packages available.

Special Millennium Golfing Breaks
Four Nights Half Board for the price of three
(Available from Sunday p.m. to Friday a.m.)
Standard Room £172.50. Large Standard
Room £187.50 Premier Room £217.50.

Situated in the beautiful Royal Forest of Dean our family
un hotel is situated adjacent to the 1st Tee. Established in
1971 it has 52 en-suite bedrooms (22 new premier rooms
opened summer 1999). Conference facilities and seminar
Rooms, and banqeting facilities for up to 160. Bar &
Restaurant open all day. 14 Golf Cars. One of the UK's
argest Golf Shops with extensive range of equipment &
Clothing.

BELTON WOODS HOTEL

Belton, Nr Grantham, Lincolnshire NG32 2LN. Tel: 01476 593200 Fax: 01476 574547

45 HOLES   PAR 72,73,27   6781,6605,1116 YARDS

TYPE OF GOLF COURSES: All Parkland

RATING: AA 4Star

TEACHING PROFESSIONAL: Joel Cant

Tel 01476 514332

DBB + 18 HOLES: From £79.00

OTHER SPECIAL GOLF PACKAGES:

Include tuition, all tailor made.

Belton Woods is set in its own 475 acre estate, set in tranquil
Lincolnshire countryside. With extensive, well appointed
facilities, the resort welcomes visitors throughout the year for
leisure and conferences.
Golfers are treated to two championship length courses
including the renowned Lakes course, complemented by the
Woodside course and the challenging Par 3 Spitfire Course.

Belton Woods is easily accessible by major road links, main line railway and East Midlands airport,
major reasons for the resort hosting the European Seniors Tour and many top-level conferences.

BRIGGATE LODGE COUNTRY HOTEL

Ermine Street, Broughton, Nr Brigg, North Lincolnshire DN20 0AQ.
Tel: 01652 650770 Fax: 01652 650495

27 HOLES   PAR 73/35   6882/3102 YARDS
TYPE OF GOLF COURSE: Undulating
Wooded and open heathland setting.
HOTEL RATING: AA 3 Star + RAC 5
Crowns
GOLF PROFESSIONAL: David Edwards
TEL: 01652 650756
B&B + 18 HOLES: From £75.00 p.p.
OTHER SPECIAL GOLF PACKAGES:
Golf Societies welcome

The Briggate Lodge Country Hotel lies within the grounds
of Forest Pines. All 86 en-suite bedrooms are equipped with
colour satellite TV, trouser press, hairdryer and direct dial
telephone. A 24 hour room service and a next day laundry
service are also available.

Golf facilities include the 27 hole championship golf course
and floodlit all-weather driving range. Forest Pines was
recently voted the best new course in England and offers
challenging play across an undulating wooded and open
heathland setting. Designed by PGA Seniors Tour player John Morgan, Forest Pines features a state of
the art irrigation system, which combined with excellent drainage ensures all year round play.

CADMORE LODGE HOTEL & COUNTRY CLUB

t. Michael's, Tenbury Wells, Worcestershire WR15 8TQ. Tel: 01584 810044 Fax: 01584 810044

akeside hotel and country club. 13 en-suite rooms
5 luxury rooms). Swimming pool (indoor), gym, sauna,
acuzzi, bowling green, spike bar and Lakeside
.estaurant. Idyllic location in rural Worcestershire.
.romatherapy and massage sessions also available.

9 HOLES	PAR 68	5132 YARDS

TYPE OF GOLF COURSE: Valley & Woodland, with feature lake
HOTEL RATING: 2 Star AA
GOLF SECRETARY: Mr Robin Farr
TEL: 01584 810306
GOLF BREAKS: 2 day break in standard rooms to include B&B, Dinner and unlimited golf £100.00 per person. In Luxury rooms 2 day break £135.00 per per person.
Society Days from £18 p.p. Daily rates £10.00 per day weekday £14.00 at weekends.

Duntisbourne Leer

THE GRANGE & LINKS HOTEL

Sandilands, Sulton-on-Sea, Lincs LN12 2RA. Tel: 01507 441334

18 HOLES	PAR 70	6086 YARDS

TYPE OF GOLF COURSE: Links

B&B + EV MEAL + 4 ROUNDS GOLF: (any 2 nights)
Sunday to Thursday £145.00 per person
Thurs/Fri - Sat/Sat - Sat/Sun £159.00 per person

OTHER SPECIAL PACKAGES:
2 night break B&B + Ev Meal (exc. golf) any two
nights £135.00 per person

MIDGET WEEK:
Sun - Thurs B&B + Ev Meal + Golf £290pp

WINTER BREAKS:
16th Oct - 1st March '01
(Ex xmas & New Year eve).

Situated two minutes walk from the beach. The Grange & Links is a privately owned family run Hotel of great charm, our motto being service, courtesy and friendliness.

The Restaurant is renowned on the East Coast and enjoys a particularly attractive setting overlooking our own beautifully kept gardens.

The Sandilands Golf Club is an 18 hole links course, par 70 with a Standard Scratch of 69 (6086 yards). The course is noted for its outstanding greens and drainage allowing year round golf.

SHRIGLEY HALL

Shrigley Park, Pott Shrigley, Nr Macclesfield, Cheshire SK10 5SB.
Tel: 01625 575757 Fax: 01625 575437

18 HOLES	PAR 71	6407 YARDS

TYPE OF GOLF COURSE: Parkland

HOTEL RATING: 4 Star

GOLF PROFESSIONAL: Tony Stevens
TEL: 01625 575626

GREENFEES: £36.00 (Mid week)
£41.00 (Weekend)

ACCOMMODATION: From £55 B&B pp

Shrigley Hall Hotel, Golf & Country Club is one of Cheshire's finest golfing venues. The 18-hole courses plays host to the Cheshire & Lancashire PGA Championship and offers breathtaking views across the cheshire Plains. Facilities include 154 room Hotel, Leisure Club, 150 visitors' lockers, private function rooms, drinks buggy and Golf & Leisurewear shop. Whether a Corporate event or a Captains weekend. Shrigley Hall has a commitment to service that will ensure your visit will not be easily forgotten.

TOFT HOUSE HOTEL

Toft, Near Bourne, Lincolnshire PE10 0JT. Tel: 01778 590614 Fax: 01778 590264

18 HOLES	PAR 72	6486 YARDS

TYPE OF GOLF COURSE: Parkland

GOLF PROFESSIONAL: Mark Jackson
TEL: 01778 590616

B&B + 18 HOLES: From £55.00 p.p.

OTHER SPECIAL GOLF PACKAGES:
Dinner, B&B + 36 holes from
£75.00 p.p.

A family run converted farmhouse,the hotel has 20 en-suite bedrooms. The course covers 107 acres of undulating land and affords picturesque views of the lake and countryside. Motorised golf buggies and electric trolleys for hire, practice area.

The Old Stocks, Stow, Glos.

ALVASTON HALL HOTEL
Middlewich Road, Nantwich, Cheshire CW5 6PD
Tel: 01270 624341 Fax: 01270 623395

HOLES: 9	YARDS: 1854	PAR: 32

BELMONT LODGE & GOLF COURSE
Belmont, Hereford HR2 9SA. Tel: 01432 352666
Fax: 01432 352717

HOLES: 18	YARDS: 6511	PAR: 72

BIDFORD GRANGE HOTEL GOLF CLUB
Stratford Road, Bidford on Avon, Warwick B50 4LY
Tel: 01789 490319 Fax: 01789 778184

HOLES: 18	YARDS: 7233	PAR: 72

HELLIDON LAKES HOTEL & COUNTRY CLUB
Hellidon, Daventry, Northamptonshire. NN1 6LN
Tel: 01327 262550 Fax: 01327 262559

HOLES: 9/18	YARDS: 2791/6600	PAR: 35/

INGON MANOR HOTEL & GOLF CLUB
Ingon Lane, Snitterfield, Stratford on Avon,
Warwickshire CV37 0QE.
Tel: 01789 731857 Fax: 01789 731657

HOLES: 18	YARDS: 6554	PAR: 72

JARVIS GLOUCESTER HOTEL & COUNTRY CLUB
Robinswood Hill, Gloucester GL4 6EA.
Tel: 01452 525653 Fax: 01452 307212

HOLES: 18	YARDS: 6100	PAR: 70

MOTTRAM HALL HOTEL
Wilmslow Road, Mottram St Andrews, Prestbury,
Cheshire SK10 4QT. Tel: 01625 828135 Fax: 01625 829284

HOLES: 18	YARDS: 7006	PAR: 72

NEW HALL COUNTRY HOUSE HOTEL
Walmley Road, Royal Sutton Coldfield B76 1QY.
Tel: 0121 378 2442 Fax: 0121 378 4637

HOLES: 9	YARDS: 773	PAR: 27

PATSHULL PARK HOTEL, GOLF & COUNTRY CLUB
Pattingham, Shropshire WV6 7HR.
Tel: 01902 700100 Fax: 01902 700374

HOLES: 18	YARDS: 6147	PAR: 72

STAVERTON PARK
Staverton, Daventry, Northants NN11 6JT.
Tel: 01327 30200 Fax: 01327 311428

HOLES: 18	YARDS: 6661	PAR: 71

Naunton

The Home Counties

Billingford Mill, Norfolk

The Home Counties

*I*f you were to draw a 50 mile radius around the centre of London, and just concentrate on playing golf in that area, then there's a safe bet you could do so for two or three months and never get bored.

The Berkshire, Sunningdale, Wentworth, Walton Heath, Swinley Forest, Stoke Poges, Ashridge, Woburn, Hankley Common, The Addington, Berkhamsted, Hanbury Manor, Moor Park, the list of great golf courses goes on and on. Small wonder that golfers who work in London prefer to commute into town. It's not the property prices – it's the fact they can be near some of these marvelous golf clubs.

Of course, Surrey is well known for it's golf. Wentworth, Sunningdale, Walton Heath, there are no shortage of great championship venues to play. And while everyone should try to play these courses at least once, even if it's getting more and more expensive to do so, there are a number of less well known courses where you can still get the flavour of Surrey golf.

Courses like Stoke Poges, Camberley Heath, Cuddington, Foxhills, Hindhead, Kingswood, Purley Downs, St George's Hill, the three Ws of Woking, Worplesdon, and West Hill. They're all good golf courses often lying just a good drive and mid iron from some of the famous Surrey fairways. Indeed, if you were to play the trio of Woking, Worplesdon, and West Hill over the course of a week, you would soon know what Surrey golf was all about – and you wouldn't have to travel too far either.

Or how about Foxhills near Chertsey? There are two good courses here with fantastic facilities on hand, including a new hotel extension. Perfect for a short break. Or what about the combination of Hankley Common, West Surrey and Hindhead, three good examples of heathland golf at its best, especially Hankley Common. It has shades of Walton Heath about it in places, is used as an Open Championship regional qualifying course and has one of the best finishing holes in inland golf.

Woburn has two lovely courses – the Dukes and the Duchess. Soon there will be a third – the Marquis – due to open in 1999. There's no hotel here, but there's plenty of accommodation roundabout. Everything from hotel to B & B accommodation. The two tree lined layouts put a premium on driving accuracy, especially the shorter Duchess layout, and they are always in good condition.

Nearby you will find Berkhamsted, a truly great, under-publicised course that is unique because it contains not one bunker. Anyone scared of the sand will love this course, although there are other dangers lurking on this fine layout. Not far away is Ashridge, where the late Sir Henry Cotton lived and worked for many years. Like Berkhamsted, this is a beautiful course in a beautiful setting that perhaps doesn't get as much press as it deserves.

Of course, being so close to the capital means that some of these layouts can be quite busy. Memberships are normally full, many with long waiting lists, however with perseverance most can still be played.

At many, too, the lunch is an essential part of the day. To sample lunch at, say, Woburn, Ashridge, Sunningdale, Walton Heath, or any number of courses in the home counties, is to sample British food at it's best. Indeed, it's the main reason you play 36 holes – for the morning 18 you look forward to the lunch, while the afternoon round is to work it off. How civilised.

King's Lynn

A47

A15

A47

Peterborough

A1(M)

Kettering

A141

Cambridgeshire
Moat House
Hotel

Newma

Northampton

Abbotsley
Golf Hotel

Bedford

Cambridge

A5

A1

Farthingstone

Beadlow
Manor

Marriott
Hanbury Manor
Hotel

A43

Mano
Grov

M1

A5

A41

Aylesbury

Luton

A10

M11

A40

St Albans

M10

Oxford

A1

Che

A420

The
Springs
Hotel

M40

Watford

M25

Maidenhead

Stoke Poges
Golf Club

Bas

Swindon

A34

Slough

LONDON

Dartford

M4

Reading

Windsor

Selsdon Par

Donnington
Grove

Newbury
Wokefield Park

Pennyhill
Park

M3

Foxhills

Croydon

Coulsdon
Manor
Hotel

Woking

M25

A34

Guildford

Oatlands
Park

A22

A3

100

Home Counties

Barnham Broom Hotel

*J*ust a few miles west of the ancient historic city of Norwich in East Anglia, the River Yare runs through a tranquil valley surrounded by Norfolk farmland. Here lies the Barnham Broom Hotel, Golf, Conference and Leisure Centre. An extensive complex with two 18 hole golf courses: The Valley par 72 and The Hill par 71, a five acre practice ground with 3 academy holes and putting green, comprehensively stocked golf shop, and extensive leisure facilities including jet stream swimming pool.

The Golf Simulator allows guests to play some of the most famous courses in the world.

The hotel offers 53 bedrooms all with private bathroom/showers, colour television, radio, direct dial telephone, trouser press, hairdryer and tea/coffee making facilities. The Flints Restaurant offers a full 'Good Morning' breakfast of hot and cold dishes, carvery at lunchtime and a choice of table d'hote and a la carte menu for dinner. The Sports Bar & Cafe offers a selection of light meals and snacks. The Valley Bar overlooks the terrace and golf courses.

Barnham Broom plays host to the Peter Ballingall Golf Schools, three and four day residential instructional courses aimed at all levels of experience. Peter Ballingall has earned the reputation as being one of the premier teachers in the game.

LOCAL ATTRACTIONS

There are many exciting and famous attractions all within easy driving distance of the hotel, including: the historic city of Norwich with its magnificent Cathedral and Castle, the Norfolk Broads, the Royal House of Sandringham, the Norfolk Lavender Fields and Blickling Hall - just a few of the many attractions surrounding the Hotel.

GOLF INFORMATION

36 hole, 6603 yard (Valley) and 6495 yard (Hill), river valley parkland course
Par 72 (Valley) & 71 (Hill)

Golf Director: Peter Ballingall

Golf Professional: Richard Wilson –
Assistant Professional Tel: 01603 759393 ext 278

Practice facilities: Outdoor driving range.

Instructions: Groups and individuals catered for. Short game facilities and 3 academy holes.

Hire: Clubs and buggies.

CARD OF THE COURSE

Hill Course			Valley Course		
1	371	Par 4	1	371	Par 4
2	212	Par 3	2	500	Par 5
3	394	Par 4	3	414	Par 4
4	432	Par 4	4	139	Par 3
5	537	Par 5	5	346	Par 4
6	135	Par 3	6	165	Par 3
7	369	Par 4	7	362	Par 4
8	402	Par 4	8	492	Par 5
9	473	Par 5	9	425	Par 4
Out	3325	Par 36	Out	3160	Par 36
10	411	Par 4	10	524	Par 5
11	173	Par 3	11	365	Par 4
12	463	Par 5	12	426	Par 4
13	409	Par 4	13	195	Par 3
14	396	Par 4	14	444	Par 4
15	403	Par 4	15	391	Par 4
16	381	Par 4	16	137	Par 3
17	152	Par 3	17	548	Par 5
18	382	Par 4	18	413	Par 4
In	3170	Par 35	In	3443	Par 36

HOTEL INFORMATION

Barnham Broom Hotel
Honingham Road
Barnham Broom
Norwich NR9 4DD
Tel: 01603 759393
Fax: 01603 758224
www: barnham-broom.co.uk
Rating: 3 Star AA & 3 Star RAC.
Rooms: 53.
Restaurants: Flints Restaurant – Table d'hote and à la Carte, Bothways snack bar.
Childcare Facilities: Morning Creche at Leisure Centre, Baby Listening.
Hair & Beauty: Hairdressers and Beauty Salon.
Fitness Facilities: Fitness studio, sauna, steam room, spa bath, swimming pool, tennis, squash.
Other Sporting Activities: Peter Ballingall Golf Schools, instructional courses run over 3 or 4 days, aimed at all levels of golfer. Indoor Golf Simulater.

TARIFF

2 night all inclusive.
Golf Package, Dinner, bed and breakfast plus three rounds of golf from £128pp

Seasonal Specials available:
Please ask for details.

DIRECTIONS

From Kings Lynn heading towards Norwich on A47 bypass East Dereham go a further 9 miles and turn off to your right following brown tourist signs for Barnham Broom. From A11 travelling from Thetford to Norwich on approaching Wymondham follow brown tourist signs through local roads to Barnham Broom.

Cambridgeshire Moat House

Situated just 5 miles from the historic city of Cambridge, and with easy access from the M25 and M11, the Cambridgeshire Moat House offers the ideal location for a relaxing break.

The hotel boasts 138 en-suite bedrooms, (including 35 brand new air-conditioned Executive Bedrooms); 9 air-conditioned Conference and Meeting rooms and a Business Centre for your convenience. Hotel residents also have full use of our excellent Club Moativation leisure facilities which includes tennis courts, a 16m swimming pool, fully equipped gymnasium, jacuzzi, steam room, sunbed* and beauty salon. (*Optional extras)

And if you're a golfer, so much the better! Our superb 18 hole Championship Golf Course has been host to a number of PGA tournaments since then. Those that played the course include Tom Watson, Nick Faldo, Seve Ballesteros, and many other top professionals.

A mature parkland course, with a number of water hazards and ditches - strategy being of the utmost importance. At over 6,700 yards from the medal tees, the course will also stretch the longest hitters. With some of the best greens in Cambridgeshire, it is a delight to play.

A well-equipped Golf Shop stocks leading brand names in equipment and clothing.

The resident PGA Professionals, led by the Head Professional - Paul Simpson - are on hand to give expert tuition to players of all abilities, from novice to scratch golfers, and to help you enjoy your break to the full. Reduced rates are available on application.

As well as golfing breaks, the Golf Club also runs Corporate Golf Days and Society Golf Days. Prices range from £16.00 up to £50.00, depending on individual requirements.

And when you're hungry, you can choose from, "Aubrey's Restaurant" (which has an extensive a la carte and table d'hote menu) or the "Gallery Bar", even try a delicious curry from our "Golf Bar".

With all the Beauty and history of Cambridgshire to explore, the Cambridgeshire Moat House offers an exceptional opportunity to get away from the hustle and bustle of every day life for golfers and non-golfers alike.

LOCAL ATTRACTIONS

Nearby Attractions:
Duxford Museum,
Huntingdon and
Newmarket racecourses,
Wimpole Hall.

GOLF INFORMATION

18 hole, 6734 yard
Undulating parkland with a lake,
ditches and many trees.
Par 72

Golf Professional: Paul Simpson
Tel:01954 780098

Practice facilities: Extensive practice areas.

Instructions: Groups and individuals catered for.

Hire: Golf clubs and buggies can be hired.

Green fees by arrangement.

CARD OF THE COURSE

1	365	Par 4	10	441	Par 4
2	521	Par 4	11	380	Par 4
3	422	Par 4	12	436	Par 4
4	361	Par 4	13	240	Par 3
5	146	Par 3	14	481	Par 5
6	376	Par 4	15	158	Par 3
7	505	Par 5	16	445	Par 4
8	188	Par 3	17	373	Par 4
9	385	Par 4	18	511	Par 5
Out	3269	Par 36	In	3465	Par 36

HOTEL INFORMATION

Cambridgeshire Moat House, Bar
Hill, Cambridge, Cambs CB3 8EU
Tel: 01954 249988
Fax: 01954 780010
Rating: AA 3 star. English Tourist
Board 4 crowns.
Rooms: 138 en-suite rooms.
Restaurants: Aubrey's restaurant, gallery bar
and golfer bar..
Other Sporting Facilities: Fully fitted gym,
indoor heated pool, sauna, steam rooms,
solarium.
Other Leisure Activities: Two hard court
tennis courts, jogging trail around golf course.
Hair & Beauty facilities: Beauty salon.
Childcare facilities: Baby listening.

TARIFF

Golfing Break
Dinner, Bed & Breakfast -
2 night - 2 round of golf
£130.00 per person.

Other Special Golf
Packages:
B&B + 18 holes: from £75.00 per
person.
Daily & Weekend Packages.
Societies welcome on application.
Visitors welcome by prior
arrangement.

DIRECTIONS

Cambridge Moat House is
easily reached whichever
part of the country you're
travelling from.

Road: M11 to A14 to
B1050 (Bar Hill).

Rail: Cambridge Station 6 miles.

Air: Cambridge Airport 8 miles;
Stanstead Airport 35 miles.

De Vere Dunston Hall Hotel

*D*unston Hall has a distinctly Elizabethan quality with its characteristic gables and scaring chimneys. The red brick mansion was built as a country retreat in 1859. This grade II listed building has been sympathetically converted and extended to provide a luxury 130 - bedroom hotel.

The Hotel offers excellent leisure facilities with an indoor pool, large gym, sauna, steam room, jacuzzi and beauty parlour, tennis courts, snooker room and a 22 - bay floodlit driving range are available.

The hotel offers a choice of three restaurants and many areas to relax.

Situated just 3½ miles from Norwich centre, just off the A47 which connects all major routes throughout East Anglia.

LOCAL ATTRACTIONS

Historic Norwich, the Norfolk Broads, the unspoilt coastline.

GOLF INFORMATION

18 hole, 6319 yard Parkland Par 71

Practice facilities: Covered driving range.

Golf Professional: Peter Briggs.

Tel: 01508 473846.

Instructions: Groups and individuals catered for.

Hire: Clubs and buggies hire available.

CARD OF THE COURSE

1	347	Par 4	10	334	Par 4
2	514	Par 5	11	315	Par 4
3	363	Par 4	12	375	Par 4
4	211	Par 3	13	341	Par 4
5	324	Par 4	14	138	Par 3
6	431	Par 4	15	591	Par 5
7	377	Par 4	16	426	Par 4
8	273	Par 4	17	560	Par 5
9	214	Par 3	18	185	Par 3
Out	3054	Par 35	In	3413	Par 36

HOTEL INFORMATION

De Vere Dunston Hall Hotel,
Ipswich Road, Norwich,
Norfolk. NR14 8PQ
Tel: 01508 470444
Fax: 01508 473846
Rating: AA 4 Star.
Rooms: 130 Bedrooms.
Restaurants: Carvery Restaurant.
Childcare Facilities: Baby listening
service.
Beauty Facilities: Beauty treatment salon.
Fitness Facilities: Large gym on three
levels, swimming pool, sauna, steam room,
jacuzzi.
Other Sporting Facilities:
Bowling, Tennis

TARIFF

Weekend Breaks
Bed & Breakfast £70.00 per person
Dinner, Bed & Breakfast (Carvery
dinner) £85.00 per person.
Single supplement £30.00.

Special Golf Packages
B&B +18 holles £90.00 pre person.
£105.00 DBB.

DIRECTIONS

From A47, take the A140
Ipswich Road. The Hotel
is situated on the right
after about 1 mile.

The Essex Golf & Country Club

*S*et in over 250 acres of countryside, The Lodge is a modern hotel linked to Eddy Shah's Essex Golf & Country Club.

It has forty two bedrooms, all en-suite with remote control satellite TV, hairdryers and trouser presses. There are two suites, both with views over the 18 hole County Course.

LOCAL ATTRACTIONS

Within thirty minutes of the Club you could find yourself exploring Britain's oldest recorded town, Colchester, and its castle and zoo. Antique lovers are spoilt for choice with the local village of Coggeshall (made famous by the 'Lovejoy' TV series) just five minutes away. A little further afield is the Suffolk town of Long Melford, with reputedly the longest high street in England and a plethora of antique shops. Constable country is only 40 minutes away with the village of Dedham set in the magnificent Stour Valley. In the other direction is the town of Sudbury, home of the painter Gainsborough.

The Essex Golf & Country Club has comfortable club house facilities. The Sports Bar and Brasserie offering a full and varied menu in a relaxed and informal environment.

Whether golf is your game or not, the combination of the friendly atmosphere and extensive range of things to do in the locality, make The Essex an ideal choice for a short break and a good base to explore the Essex and Suffolk countryside.

Whilst residing at The Lodge, you receive complimentary use of the indoor heated swimming pool, spa bath, sauna and steam room. You will also benefit from privilege golf, tennis, aerobic and gymnasium rates. Golf and tennis coaching is available on either an individual or group basis, further details are available on request.

GOLF INFORMATION

18 hole (County) 6982 yard, 9 hole (Garden) 2190 yard parkland course Par 73 & 34

Golf Professional: Mark Spooner
Tel: 01787 224466

Practice facilities: Covered floodlit driving range.

Instruction: Groups and individuals catered for. Video Studio. Covered practice bunker.

Hire: Clubs and buggies

CARD OF THE COURSE					
1	566	Par 5	10	508	Par 5
2	394	Par 4	11	154	Par 3
3	470	Par 4	12	429	Par 4
4	351	Par 4	13	431	Par 4
5	143	Par 3	14	190	Par 3
6	395	Par 4	15	368	Par 4
7	189	Par 3	16	410	Par 4
8	523	Par 5	17	563	Par 5
9	399	Par 4	18	499	Par 5
Out	3430	Par 36	In	3552	Par 37

HOTEL INFORMATION

Essex Golf & Country Club
Earls Colne
Colchester CO6 2NS
Tel: 01787 224466
Fax: 01787 224410
Rating: Tourist Board – 3 Crowns commended
Rooms: 42.
Restaurants: Informal Sports Bar & Brasserie
Childcare: On site 5 day nursery. Baby listening – free of charge.
Hair and Beauty: Independently run salons, bookings advisable.

TARIFF

Room Only – £45 per room, per night single, £50 per room, per night twin/double, £65 per room, per night suite.
Weekend B+B – £50 per room (Single), £60 per room (twin/double), £70 per room (suite).

Special Golf Packages: Phone for details.

Other Special Golf Packages – Group packages available for 6 or more people.

DIRECTIONS

From A12 - take A120 sliproad off A12 signed for Stanstead and Braintree. Follow A120 for 4 miles, after signs for Coggeshall you will reach crossroads. Turn right onto B1024 signed for Earls Colne. Follow B1024 for 2 miles, past The Bird In Hand pub. The Essex is signed on the left hand side, taking you separate onto the airfield.

Farthingstone Hotel & Golf Course

*F*arthingstone Hotel & Golf Course lies between two woods at the head of a picturesque valley, deep in gently rolling Northamptonshire countryside. Opened in August 1973, Farthingstone was developed from rough pasture surrounding Manor Farm. This challenging Championship course now extends to 6299 yards from the competition tees. Its conception and development have ensured that its character is not that of the generic, market research positioned facility, that many new courses have become. Instead, Farthingstone is a unique, unusually located and beautifully tranquil course.

The course has been designed utilising the natural form and features of the land, it is not a course suffering an artificial and false landscape, created by modern construction machinery. Farthingstone's design and its natural, organic development have ensured that the natural features and forms of the land have been retained and made use of, to test and challenge your skills.

Farthingstone boasts a comfortable sixteen bedroom hotel plus a charming and welcoming bar restaurant for a relaxing drink and meal.

Additional facilities which can be enjoyed by guests and visitors are snooker room and squash court, both of which are on site.

The combined facilities of the golf course and hotel allow Farthingstone to offer a full range of golfing packages for groups and societies, all at excellent rates.

LOCAL ATTRACTIONS

Local attractions include Silverstone Circuit, Towcester Racecourse, Althorpe House, Sulgrave Manor, Cannons Ashby, and the Old Dairy Craft Centre. Northampton, Milton Keynes, Daventry & Towcester, are all within easy travelling distance. Slightly further afield the historic towns of Stratford Upon Avon, Warwick, Leamington Spa, and Oxford.

GOLF INFORMATION

18 hole 6299 yard, Parkland course Par 70

Golf Professional: Tel: 01327 361533

Hire: Clubs and buggies hire available.

CARD OF THE COURSE

1	378	Par 4	10	375	Par 4
2	181	Par 3	11	198	Par 3
3	393	Par 4	12	398	Par 4
4	488	Par 4	13	213	Par 3
5	184	Par 3	14	606	Par 5
6	294	Par 4	15	183	Par 3
7	482	Par 5	16	361	Par 4
8	343	Par 4	17	392	Par 4
9	343	Par 4	18	487	Par 5
Out	3086	Par 35	In	3213	Par 35

HOTEL INFORMATION

Farthingstone Hotel & Golf Course, Farthingstone, Nr Towcester, Northants. NN12 8HA
Tel: 01327 361291
Fax: 01327 361645
www: www.farthingstone.co.uk

Rooms: Comfortable 16 twin or double bedded rooms, and have ensuite bathrooms together with separate toilet, tea and coffee making facilities, colour television, radio alarm, and telephone..
Restaurants: Carvery Restaurant and Bar.
Fitness Facilities: Squash court.
Other Sporting Facilities:
Two full size snooker tables, 1 pool table.

TARIFF

B&B + 18 holes:
£65.00.
Weekend Breaks:
B&B single occomodation £45.00, Double accomodation £65.00.

Other Special Golf Packages:
Golfing breaks midweek £69.00 pp/pn (2 rounds of golf, dinner B&B)

Golfing breaks weekends £79.00 pp/pn (2 rounds of golf, dinner B&B).

DIRECTIONS

From M1 Junction 16 (Northampton) Travel West on the A45 towards Daventry. At Weedon traffic lights (junction of A4 &A5) turn left, turn immediate right in top Weedon village, follow road through village, up steep hill and continue through open countryside (4 miles) until you reach Farthingstone village. At junction turn right, travel through village. The entrance to the course is at the bottom of the hill.
From M40 Junction 11(Banbury) Travel East on A422 towards Brackley, at first roundabout take B4525, follow road until left hand junction to Thorpe Mandeville, follow road through villages of Moreton Pinkney, Canons Ashby, and Adstone. At Maidford turn left into village. Go through Maidford, turn right at first junction towards Farthingstone, at junction by church turn left through village and down hill. The entrance is at the bottom of the hill on the left.

The Links Country Park Hotel

*S*et in 40 acres of lightly wooded coastal parkland, designated an area of outstanding natural beauty, 'The Links' offers a warm welcome, a peaceful escape from everyday pressures and the opportunity to relax and unwind.

Proudly independent, 'The Links' has retained high standards of personal service. An imaginative menu is prepared from fresh, local produce, and the extensive wine list caters for a wide variety of tastes.

All 43 bedrooms are comfortable, well appointed, with en-suite facilities. The Garden Rooms offer larger accommodation, ideal for families. For that really special occasion, luxuriously appointed executive rooms can make your break at 'The Links' a truly memorable event.

The hotel has its own 9-hole golf course, an all-weather tennis court, a nearby pony trekking centre and miles of beach and footpaths giving ample opportunity to enjoy the bracing sea air and unspoilt north Norfolk countryside. An indoor heated swimming pool, sauna and fast tanning sun bed offer year round activity whatever the weather. The hotel is also well-equipped to accommodate sales conferences and similar events.

GOLF INFORMATION

9 hole, 2421 yard seaside parkland course

Par 33

Golf Professional: Lee Patterson

Tel: 01263 838215

Hire: Clubs and buggies

CARD OF THE COURSE		
1	197	Par 3
2	502	Par 5
3	105	Par 3
4	426	Par 4
5	217	Par 3
6	320	Par 4
7	121	Par 3
8	265	Par 4
9	268	Par 4
Out	2421	Par 33

HOTEL INFORMATION

The Links Country Park Hotel & Golf Club
Sandy Lane
West Runton
Cromer
Norfolk NR27 9QH
Tel: 01263 838383
Fax: 01263 838264

Rating: English Tourist Board 3 Star.
Rooms: 43.
Restaurants: Edwardian Style – French, English and Seafood.
Hair and Beauty: In local village or visiting hairdresser.
Other Sporting Facilities: Indoor heating pool, all weather tennis court, sauna & solarium.
Other Leisure Activities: Specialised weekends organised for winter months – Dates to be announced.

ALL LEISURE FACILITIES, INCLUDING GOLF, FREE TO HOTEL RESIDENTS.

TARIFF

Seasonal rates on application starting at **£42.50 B&B** per person (min 2 nights)

Dinner B&B From £60.00.

Special rates for golf societies - other special golf packages.

DIRECTIONS

From Blakeney: turn right off A149 in the centre of West Runton following the Hotel & Golf Course sign.

From Holt: left off A148 at Aylmerton through Roman Camp to West Runton.

From Norwich: follow A140 until is joins A149 through Cromer and East Runton following Hotel & Golf Course sign.

Marriott Hanbury Manor Hotel & Country Club

*J*ust 25 miles north of London and just 15 minutes from the M25, this historic 5 star resort is often known as "London's favourite Hotel and Country Club".

Each of the 96 bedrooms has its own distinctive style and surrounds you in traditional luxury yet with all the facilities of a modern hotel. The Zodiac Restaurant was the Hanbury family's summer drawing room and serves as the main gourmet restaurant for traditional English and French cuisine. Alternatively, a more relaxed dining experience Vardons Restaurant and Bar is ideal.

The 18 hole championship golf course, designed by Jack Nicklaus II, offers cleverly sited hazards, some of the best greens in Britain and has hosted the Women's European Open in 1996, the Alamo English Open in 1997, and Compass Group English Open in 1999 National Car Rental English Open in 1998 - if you wish to play the course don't forget to pack your handicap certificate as you will be required to show it. A practice ground and putting green are also available.

Hanbury Manor can offer an extensive range of leisure facilities, and with echoes of ancient Rome, the large indoor heated pool and giant spa bath are star attractions, together with aroma baths, solaria, steam rooms and sauna. Tennis, croquet, dance, yoga, aerobics and a gymnasium are available plus beauty treatment rooms.

LOCAL ATTRACTIONS

Visit the Verulanium Museum in St Albans, or the historic Houses of Hatfield and Knebworth. A little further afield is the Imperial War Museum at Duxford or take a trip into Cambridge or even London. Closer are the attractions of Hertford, Paradise Wildlife Park and Lee Valley Park.

GOLF INFORMATION

18 hole, 6622 yard, Hanbury Course

Par 72

Practice facilities: Practice ground, putting green, chipping green.

Instructions: Tuition and video facilites.

Golf Shop: Fully stocked with latest fashions.

Hire: Trolley, buggy and club hire.
HANDICAP CERTIFICATES REQUIRED.

CARD OF THE COURSE
White Tees

1	314	Par 4	10	383	Par 4
2	529	Par 5	11	181	Par 3
3	425	Par 4	12	532	Par 5
4	167	Par 3	13	379	Par 4
5	456	Par 4	14	371	Par 4
6	164	Par 3	15	396	Par 4
7	341	Par 4	16	177	Par 3
8	425	Par 4	17	486	Par 5
9	528	Par 5	18	368	Par 4
Out	3349	Par 36	In	3273	Par 36

HOTEL INFORMATION

Marriott Hanbury Manor Hotel & Country Club
Ware,
Hertfordshire SG12 9SD
Tel: 01920 487722
Fax: 01920 487692

Rooms: 96.
Restaurants: The Zodiac Restaurant, Vardon Restaurant Cocktail Bar.
Hair and Beauty: 6 beauty treatment rooms.
Other Fitness Facilities: Indoor heated swimming pool, steam rooms, sauna, dance studio with a variety of classes, cardiovascular gymnasium, resistance gymnasium, solaria.
Other Sporting Facilities: Tennis courts, croquet lawn, snooker table.

TARIFF

BED & BREAKFAST
(Mon-Sun)

Prices start from **£130.00** per person per night, including a round of golf. Based on two sharing.

DIRECTIONS

Take Junction 25 from the M25 and the A10 northbound to Hertford. Remain on the A10 for 12 miles. The Hotel is situated on the left hand side just past the town sign of Thundridge. Stanstead Airport is 16 miles away and Heathrow 48 miles.

Oatlands Park Hotel

*O*atlands Park Hotel is a four-star country house hotel set in the heart of the Surrey countryside, yet is only a 25-minute train journey from London's West End, with easy access to both Gatwick and Heathrow airports.

Oatlands Park boasts a wide range of accommodation – from the 'superior' rooms to the larger 'deluxe' rooms and suites. Many enjoy beautiful views over the extensive grounds and Broadwater Lake.

Our elegant Broadwater restaurant boasts a creative a la carte menu and an excellent table d'hôte menu. The resident pianist is here on Friday and Saturday evenings and Sunday lunchtimes.

Once surrounded by an 18-hole parkland golf course, the current owners of the hotel have long wished to return the remaining land to its former use and have done so by constructing a challenging Par 3 loop of 9 holes.

Using the profile of some of the existing holes the new course still retains the features of a parkland course. Three holes are located at the rear of the hotel along the shores of the Broadwater Lake, with the remaining six playing in front of the hotel along the tree lined drive.

An ideal course for the pure beginner, or a test of skill for the more advanced golfer trying to break par.

LOCAL ATTRACTIONS

The assets of the area are countless;

Places of historical interest include; Windsor Castle, Hampton Court, Guildford Cathedral and Brooklands Museum.

Places of natural beauty & gardens include; Wisley Gardens, Royal Botanical Gardens at Kew and Painshill Park.

Places of a sporting interest include; Twickenham, Wimbledon, Sandown Park, Kempton Park and Royal Ascot.

Places for the children include; Thorpe Park, Chessington World of Adventures, Gatwick Zoo and Legoland.

GOLF INFORMATION

9 hole, 1172 yard parkland course

Par 27

Instructions: Groups and individuals catered for.

Hire: Clubs

CARD OF THE COURSE		
1	137	Par 3
2	95	Par 3
3	100	Par 3
4	127	Par 3
5	198	Par 3
6	85	Par 3
7	106	Par 3
8	215	Par 3
9	109	Par 3
Total	1172	Par 27

HOTEL INFORMATION

Oatlands Park Hotel
Oatlands Drive,
Weybridge,
Surrey KT13 9HB
Tel: 01932 847242
Fax: 01932 842252
Rating: 4 Star

Rooms: 136.
Restaurants: Broadwater restaurant – English and International cuisine, also light meals in main lounge bar.
Other Fitness Facilities: Fully equipped 'Pulse' gymnasium.
Other Sporting Facilities: 1 all-weather hard tennis court.
Other Leisure Activities: 1 antiques fair per month on a Sunday. Various weekends throughout year – Bridge, Jazz + Golf tuition.

TARIFF

Monday – Thursday
Singles from   £117.50
Doubles from   £165.00

Friday – Sunday
Singles from £60.00
Doubles from £90.00

All prices inclusive of VAT @17.5% and Full English Breakfast

DIRECTIONS

Exit M25 at junction 11 following signs for Chertsey. Proceed along A317 following signs for Weybridge. Follow the road through Weybridge High Street. Follow through into Monument Hill to mini roundabout. Turn left into Oatlands Drive and the hotel is 500 yards on the left.

SURREY

Stocks Golf & Country Club

Stocks Hotel & Country Club is a Georgian Mansion set within an estate of 182 acres surrounded by 10,000 acres of National Trust Land located between Ashridge Forest and the Chiltern Hills. The highly acclaimed golf course is complemented by a Hotel offering exemplary service and style. The whole is a combination of great beauty and charm.

Stocks Golf Course has been sympathetically constructed to follow the natural terrain and features breathtaking views and a wealth of natural beauty. Stocks is a Championship quality course that enjoys. 62 tees allowing for a variety of configurations from 5595 yards (ladies) to over 7000 yards.

Built on a predominantly chalk subsoil which allows genuine year round play, The course has never been closed due to rain nor have winter greens been required.

LOCAL ATTRACTIONS

Whipsnade Zoo, Woburn Safari Park, Ashridge Forest.

GOLF INFORMATION

18 hole, 7016 yard parkland course Par 72

Golf Professional: Peter Lane
Tel: 01442 851491

Practice facilities: Driving Range, practice bunker, putting green, chipping green.

Instructions: Groups and individuals catered for.

Hire: Clubs and buggies.

CARD OF THE COURSE

1	371	Par 4	10	196	Par 3
2	226	Par 3	11	366	Par 4
3	474	Par 4	12	317	Par 4
4	424	Par 4	13	386	Par 4
5	378	Par 4	14	505	Par 5
6	601	Par 5	15	530	Par 5
7	372	Par 4	16	445	Par 4
8	563	Par 5	17	164	Par 3
9	231	Par 3	18	467	Par 4
Out	3640	Par 36	In	3376	Par 36

HOTEL INFORMATION

Stocks Golf & Country Club
Stocks Road, Aldbury, Nr Tring,
Hertfordshire. MP23 5 RX
Tel: 01442 851341
Fax: 01442 851253
Rooms: 18.

Restaurants: 2 - Table D'Hote & Brasserie style.
Fitness Facilities: Very large jacuzzi, sauna, steamroom, outdoor heated swimming pool.

Othe Sporting Facilities: Tennis (Hard courts).

Other Leisure Activities: Various - on application.

TARIFF

B&B + 18 holes
On application.

Other Special Golf Packages
On application.

Weekend Breaks
On application.

DIRECTIONS

From the South
Leave M25 at Junction 20, follow A41 for Aylesbury. Leave at Tring Junction. Follow signs for BR Station, continue past station into Aldbury. Turn left at duck pond into Stocks road.

From the North
Leave M1 at Junction 11. Follow A505 through Dunstable towards Ivinghoe. Turn left at 'T' junction, then take 1st left into Stocks Road at sharp right hand bend.

DONNINGTON GROVE COUNTRY CLUB

Grove Road, Donnington, Newbury Berks RG14 2CA. Tel: 01635 581000 Fax: 01635 552259

18 HOLES	PAR 72	7045 YARDS
TYPE OF GOLF COURSE: Parkland		
GOLF PROFESSIONAL: Gareth Williams		
TEL: 01635 551975		
B&B + 18 HOLES: On application		
OTHER SPECIAL GOLF PACKAGES:		
On application		

Donnington Grove is set in a secluded position on the outskirts of Newbury. The championship golf course designed by Dave Thomas (designer of The Belfry) is aesthetically pleasing and exciting to play. The clubhouse and hotel is located within a beautifully renovated 18th century Gothic house. Facilities available include buggies, tennis courts, conference rooms, bar and an excellent restaurant whose menu includes the finest Japanese cuisine and European dishes. A-la-carte and set meals available.

THE MANOR OF GROVES HOTEL, GOLF & COUNTRY CLUB

High Wych, Sawbridgeworth, Hertfordshire CM21 0LA. Tel: 01279 600777 Fax: 01279 600374
Golf Club Tel: 01279 722333 Fax: 01279 726972

18 HOLES	PAR 71	6280 YARDS
TYPE OF GOLF COURSE: Woodland and		
Parkland		
B&B:		
Single £90 Double £105		
Delux Single £105 Delux Double £130		

A Georgian manor house set in 150 acres of rolling Hertfordshire countryside, which in itself has been developed into an 18 hole championship golf course. The 6280 yards, par 71 course is a mixture of woodland and parkland and provides a stern challenge to golfers of all standards.

There are 32 luxurious bedrooms all individually decorated with luxury marble bathrooms and furnished in the style of a private country house. The Colonnade Restaurant offers a wide range of international cuisine and an extensive wine list.

THE SPRINGS HOTEL & GOLF CLUB

Wallingford Road, North Stoke, Wallingford, Oxfordshire. OX10 6BE Tel: 01491 836687
Fax: 01491 827312 Email: info@thespringshotel.co.uk Web site: www.thespringshotel.co.uk

18 HOLES	PAR 72	6470 YARDS
TYPE OF GOLF COURSE: Riverside & Parkland		
HOTEL RATING: 3 Star		
GOLF PROFESSIONAL: Leigh Atkins		
TEL PRO SHOP: 01491 823310		
B&B + 18 HOLES: From £65.00 per person per night (Based on 2 people sharing a room) Other special packages available.		

The Springs Hotel is a fine example of a Victorian Tudor style Country House. Built in 1874, it overlooks a spring-fed lake in it's own majestic gardens. The Springs has 31 guestrooms and suites, all of their own individual style.

It is the ideal place for a relaxing gathering, meal or overnight stay following your efforts on the golf course. Leisure facilities include a sauna, outdoor heated swimming pool and a croqet lawn. Fishing is also available on the banks of the river Thames.

Offically designated an area of outstanding natural beauty, 133 acres of parkland bordered by the river Thames - makes an exquisite and tranquil setting for the Springs Golf Course. Within this lie three lakes and challenging wetlands areas to add to the attractions of the 18 hole, par 72 course.

Ely, Cambridgeshire

SELSDON PARK HOTEL & GOLF COURSE

Addington Road, Sanderstead, South Croydon CR2 8YA. Tel: 0181 657 8811 Fax: 0181 657 3401

18 HOLES	PAR 73	6473 YARDS

TYPE OF GOLF COURSE: Parkland
HOTEL RATING: 4 Star delux
GOLF PROFESSIONAL: Mr Malcolm Churchill
TEL: 0181 657 4129
B&B + 18 HOLES: £99 DBB + 1 round golf
OTHER SPECIAL GOLF PACKAGES: Lots of packages, please call.

The Hotel was purchased in March 1997 by Principal Hotels, who have added this distinctive property to its expanding portfolio of traditional hotels. Since then a £2.5 million refurbishment has transformed the extensive facilities, making the Hotel one of the highest graded in the area. The hotel now has 205 bedrooms and suites and a considerable range of conference and banqueting rooms.

The 18 hole championship course laid out by five times British Open Champion J.H. Taylor. The course is not perhaps for the novice, although it provides a stimulating challenge to low and high handicappers alike.

STOKE POGES GOLF CLUB

Stoke Park, Park Road, Stoke Poges, Buckinghamshire SL2 4PG.
Tel: 01753 717171 Fax: 01753 717181 Email: info@stokeparkclub.com

27 HOLES	PAR 71	6600 YARDS

TYPE OF GOLF COURSE: Mature Parkland
RATING: Gold Award from English Tourist Board
GOLF PROFESSIONAL: David Woodward
TEL: 01753 717172
B&B + 18 HOLES: £215 per person.
Visitors fees available on request.

A multi million pound refurbishment has been completed to Stoke Poges incorporating 21 bedrooms. Every room has a superb view of the magnificent golf course and gardens, designed by Capability Brown. Many rooms have open fires and private balconies and all offer exquisite bathrooms with heated marble floors,wrought iron baths and marble showers. The golf course was designed in 1908 by Harry Shapland Colt and is probably Colt's finest parkland creation. The 7th may be the celebrated hole, inspiring Alister MacKenzie to design the notorious 12th hole at Augusta National. The club's facilities also include 9 outdoor tennis courts.

THORPENESS HOTEL & GOLF CLUB

Thorpeness, Aldeburgh, Suffolk IP16 4NH. 01728 452176 Fax: 01728 453868

18 HOLES	PAR 69	6271 YARDS

TYPE OF GOLF COURSE: Coastal Heathland
GOLF PROFESSIONAL: Frank Hill
TEL: 01728 454926
B&B + 18 HOLES: From £50.00
OTHER SPECIAL GOLF PACKAGES: Over 55's ladies, gents, Xmas, New Year & Easter.

30 newly refurbished en-suite rooms, bars, restaurant, snooker, tennis, new library and card room quiet lounge overlooking the lake. Further accommodation and dining at The Dolphin Inn, our sister hotel in Thorpeness village. We cater for individual golf breaks, societies and corporate days.
Challenging course, handicap certificate mandatory.

Thames at Cookham, Berkshire

ABBOTSLEY GOLF HOTEL

Eynesbury Hardwicke, St Neots, Cambridgeshire PE19 4XN
Tel: 01480 474000 Fax: 01480 471018

HOLES: 18	YARDS: 5997	PAR: 72

Newmarket Races, Suffolk

BEADLOW MANOR HOTEL
Beadlow, Nr Shefford, Bedfordshire SG17 5PH
Tel: 01525 860800 Fax: 01525 861345

HOLES: 2 x 18 **YARDS:** 5763 / 6342 **PAR:** 71 / 73

COULSDON MANOR
Coulsdon Court Road, Coulsdon, Surrey. CR5 2LL
Tel: 0181 668 0414 Fax: 0181 668 0342

HOLES: 18 **YARDS:** 6037 **PAR:** 70

FIVE LAKES HOTEL GOLF & COUNTRY CLUB
Colchester Road, Tolleshunt Knight, Malden, Essex CM9 8HX.
Tel: 01621 868888 Fax: 01621 862326

HOLES: 18/18 **YARDS:** 6767/6188 **PAR:** 72/71

FOXHILLS
Foxhills, Ottershaw, Surrey KT16 0EL. Tel: 01932 87 20 50
Fax: 01932 87 47 62

HOLES: 45 **YARDS:** 6734 / 6429 / 1143 **PAR:** 73 / 72 / 27

PENNYHILL PARK HOTEL & COUNTRY CLUB
London Road, Bagshot, Surrey GU19 5ET
Tel: 01276 471774 Fax: 01276 475570

HOLES: 9 **YARDS:** 4110 **PAR:** 34

UFFORD PARK HOTEL GOLF & LEISURE
Yarmouth Road, Ufford, Woodbridge, Suffolk IP12 1QW.
Tel: 01394 383555 Fax: 01394 383582

HOLES: 18 **YARDS:** 6325 **PAR:** 71

WOKEFIELD PARK GOLF CLUB
Wokefield Park, Mortimer, Reading, Berkshire RG7 3AG.
Tel: 0118 933 4000 Fax: 0118 933 4031

HOLES: 18 **YARDS:** 7000 **PAR:** 72

WENSUM VALLEY HOTEL GOLF & COUNTRY CLUB
Beech Avenue, Taverham, Norwich, Norfolk NR8 6HP
Tel: 01603 261012

HOLES: 18 **YARDS:** 6172 **PAR:** 72

Yorkshire and the Northeast

Yorkshire and the Northeast

We normally don't think of Yorkshire and England's Northeast coast as a top class area for golf. Usually our minds wander to the Kingdom of Fife, to Lancashire, Kent, Ayrshire. It takes a long time before we get round to Yorkshire and further "up coast, like".

That part of England is normally associated with cricket, good bitter and hearty lunches. Golf usually comes last on the agenda. It shouldn't, though, for it contains some of the best courses in these isles.

This is a very large area and one you won't want to whizz round. Ideally you would like two weeks to see all the top courses, so you may just have to come back another time. Shame.

If you're going to start anywhere in the Northeast, then it makes sense to start where Ryder Cup history was recorded in this part of the world. Lindrick is the historical spot in question, for it was here, in 1957, that Great Britain & Ireland, after seven straight defeats, defeated America.

It was heady stuff, back then, for the Ryder Cup had become a one sided affair. Little did Max Faulkner, Peter Alliss, Ken Bousfield and the rest of the team know that it would be another 14 matches before the Americans were overcome again.

Lindrick is classic English heathland golf. Situated on Lindrick Common, the layout is played over fairways bordered by gorse, with oak and silver birch trees thrown in. A must for anyone interested in the Ryder Cup and wishing to play one of the classics of English golf.

Not too far away from Lindrick you will find Ilkey. This also has connections with the Ryder Cup, even if the great match has not been staged there. Ilkley's fairways, you see, were once trod by a young Colin Montgomerie, the man who earned the winning half point for Europe at Valderrama in 1997.

Ilkley's professional Bill Ferguson was the man responsible for moulding the young Montgomerie's game, and the canny old pro is still there to take your green fees when you arrive to play this pretty course.

Set at the base of the escarpment that rises to Ilkley Moor, the course is wooded and the River Wharfe comes into play on the first six holes. With only two par-5s and five par-3s, par is 69. However, don't expect it to be a pushover. It isn't.

Neither is Moortown, another course with Ryder Cup connections. It was at Moortown in 1929 that the first official Ryder Cup was played. Great Britain and Ireland took the honours that year, with a 7-5 win over the Americans.

Typical of Yorkshire golf, Moortown is classic heath/moorland in character, with lots of heather and gorse to catch any wayward shot. After several changes to an original designed by Dr Alister Mackenzie, the course now measures over 7,000 yards with a par of 72 and a SSS of 73.

Not far away you will find Yorkshire classics in the shape of Alwoodley, Pannal and Moor Allerton, all within a short drive of the city of Leeds. These are all good demanding courses, where you will have to work hard to match your handicap – just as a Yorkshireman would expect you to do.

For example, Pannal's scorecard reads to a par of 72, but the Standard Scratch Score is 73, and that's probably being just a wee bit stingy. Played over a moorland plateau, if you catch it on a windy day, as is often the case, then you will struggle to match your handicap. The same can be said of Alwoodley, especially from the back tees.

Further away from Leeds, just outside the city of York, you will find Fulford golf club. For years – 18 to be precise – this was the venue of the Benson & Hedges International Open, until the event was moved to St Mellion.

Lack of length was said to be the reason for moving the tournament, although handicap golfers will still find it long enough, and narrow, too. For the fairways aren't exactly generous. But the greens are receptive to a good shot and are usually in excellent condition. Perfect for a day out.

So, too, is Ganton, further up the road towards Scarborough.

This fine course also has Ryder Cup connections having hosted the 1949 match, when the Americans won 7-5.

Ganton is often mistakenly thought of as a links by people who have never visited the course. Situated some 10 miles from the sea, it is anything but – however, it does contain links characteristics. A sandy base and tight fairway lies will make you think you are playing by the sea when you play Ganton.

This is only a smattering of Yorkshire golf. There is more, much more. The fun is in exploring the area to find its hidden gems.

That's also part of the fun of venturing farther up the coastline and north of Yorkshire, to Northumbria. Here, too, you will find plenty of good golf to whet your appetite. From Seaton Carew in the south to Berwick-upon-Tweed at the end of the country, there are a number of challenging courses in between. Enough to make that county a separate holiday of its own. Brancepeth Castle, Eaglescliff, Morpeth, Hexham, Slaley Hall, try them all if you have the time. Particularly Slaley Hall, where the European Tour has held a tournament for the past two years. This course, too, could eventually have Ryder Cup ties for it's been hinted at by Ken Schofield, executive director of the European Tour, that this could be a possible venue for the 2009 match. Now there's a trip to think of – play the Ryder Cup venues of the Northeast. One thing's for sure, you wouldn't be bored.

Yorkshire & North East

Page

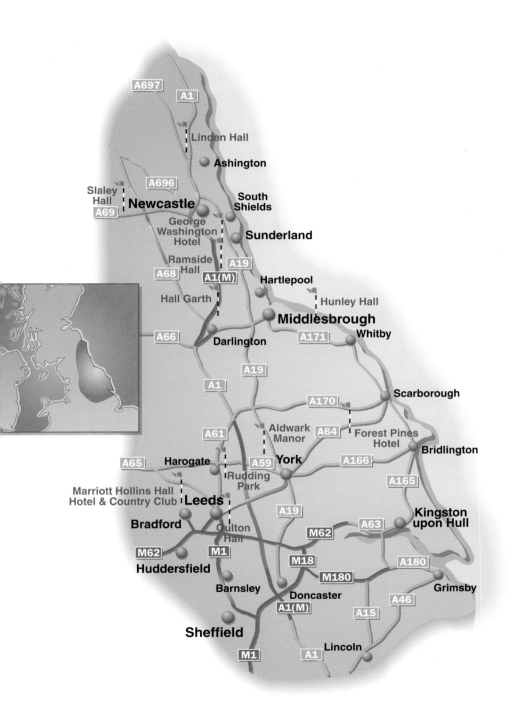

A697
A1
Linden Hall
Ashington
A696
Slaley
Hall
A69 Newcastle
South
Shields
George
Washington
Hotel
Sunderland
Ramside
Hall A19
A68
A1(M)
Hartlepool
Hall Garth
Hunley Hall
A66
Middlesbrough
Darlington
A171
Whitby
A19
A1
Scarborough
A170
A61
Aldwark
Manor
A64
Forest Pines
Hotel
A65
Harogate
A59
York
A166
Bridlington
Rudding
Park
A165
Marriott Hollins Hall
Hotel & Country Club
Leeds
Bradford
Oulton
Hall
A19
Kingston
upon Hull
M62
A63
M62
M1
M18
A180
Huddersfield
M180
Barnsley
Doncaster
Grimsby
A1(M)
A46
Sheffield
A15
M1
A1
Lincoln

131

George Washington Golf & Country Club

*S*et in a tranquil area within its own 18-hole championship golf course, the George Washington Golf & Country Club is a stylish and comfortable hotel, perfect for both business and leisure breaks.

With easy access to the nearby cities of Newcastle, Sunderland, Durham and the Tyne Tunnel, the George Washington is well placed for the nightlife of Newcastle and for visiting the Metro Centre, one of Europe's largest shopping centres.

The hotel offers 103 en-suite bedrooms, including large executive rooms, all with colour television with in-house movies, trouser-press, hairdryer, tea and coffee making facilities and 24 hour room service. Other facilities include a lounge bar, restaurant, and well-equipped health and fitness club, together with indoor swimming pool.

Our brightest, naturally lit Washington Suite offers excellent banqueting facilities for up to 180 people, or can take up to 200 delegates for a theatre style presentation and has its own bar. The private section of Lincoln's Restaurant is also popular for banquets and theatre style presentations. For smaller meetings or private dinners for up to 20, the Chairman's and Director's suites make ideal venues. We also have syndicate rooms available for smaller meetings.

Our Business Centre gives delegates all the facilities they need to work when away from their office including secretarial, fax and photocopying services.

Whether your visit is purely leisure or linked to business, you will receive high quality service and experience a refreshing and friendly atmosphere at the George Washington Golf & Country Club.

LOCAL ATTRACTIONS

George Washington is well placed to visit, Newcastle, Sunderland, Durham and the Tyne & Wear Tunnel, as weel as enjoy the night life Newcastle or visit the Metro Centre, one of Europe's largest shopping centres.

GOLF INFORMATION

18 hole, 6604 yard parkland course
Par 73

Golf Professional: Warren Marshall
Tel: 0191 4178346

CARD OF THE COURSE					
1	492	Par 5	10	376	Par 4
2	227	Par 3	11	495	Par 5
3	502	Par 5	12	368	Par 4
4	396	Par 4	13	194	Par 4
5	516	Par 5	14	377	Par 4
6	352	Par 4	15	152	Par 3
7	385	Par 4	16	373	Par 4
8	369	Par 4	17	494	Par 5
9	174	Par 3	18	362	Par 4
Out 3413 Par 37			In 3191 Par 36		

TYNE & WEAR

HOTEL INFORMATION

George Washington Golf &
Country Club,
Stone Cellar Road,
High Usworth,
District 12, Washington,
Tyne & Wear. NE37 1PH
Tel: 0191 402 9988
Fax: 0191 415 1166
Rating: AA 3 Star, RAC 4 Star,
ETB – 4 Crowns commended
Rooms: 103 ensuite rooms.
Restaurants: Lincoln's Restaurant
and Bar.

Fitness Facilities: Heath and fitness club
together with indoor swimming pool.

TARIFF

B&B + 18 holes
£50 (twin/double) £70
(single)

**Other special golf
packages:**
£60.00 (dinner, bed & breakfast +
1 round of golf - twin/double)
£80.00 (dinner, bed & breakfast +
1 round of golf - single)

DIRECTIONS

From A1 (M) (Junction 65)
onto A194 (M). Turn off on
A195 sign posted Washington
North. Take last exit off
roundabout for Washington.
Turn right at mini-roundabout.
The hotel is 0.5 miles on the
right hand side.

Rail: Newcastle Central, 5 miles
Air: Newcastle, 12 miles.

133

Marriott Hollins Hall Hotel & Country Club

*M*arriott Hollins Hall has a passion for golf. Our 6671 yard course is a masterpiece in tactical design. With very little land movement and a consideration for the local wildlife the course has been built in natural heathland amongst the beautiful Yorkshire moors and dales and it is no suprise that Mark James has described it as 'the best new course I've seen in a long time'.

It is majestically challenging and classically designed in the spirit of the game.

Set in its own tranquil surroundings, the Marriott Hollins Hall Hotel & Country Club is perfectly located in the heart of Yorkshire. It is within easy reach of the M62 and a short drive away from the business and shopping centres of Leeds and Bradford. It is also only ten minutes from the airport.

Those on business will find a welcome retreat in the Hotel's 200-acre site, with its fully equipped leisure complex and extensive meeting facilities.

Hollins Hall was constructed bearing Elizabethan lines and styles in 1878. Today with the quiet tranquillity of the graceful surroundings combined with the very latest in health and fitness and golf activities, the hotel has become a relaxing and peaceful destination.

LOCAL ATTRACTIONS

For anyone on a leisure break this is an ideal base from which to explore local attractions such as Salt's Mill, Saltaire, Bronte Country, The Yorkshire Dales, Emmerdale Country and The Woolpack.

GOLF INFORMATION

18 hole, 6671 yard heathland/woodland course

Par 71

Practice facilities: Outdoor driving range.

Instructions: Groups and individuals catered for.

Hire: Clubs, shoes and buggies.

Other - Golf concierge.

CARD OF THE COURSE

1	322	Par 4	10	512	Par 5
2	382	Par 4	11	455	Par 4
3	549	Par 5	12	365	Par 4
4	200	Par 3	13	199	Par 3
5	427	Par 4	14	363	Par 4
6	424	Par 4	15	161	Par 3
7	527	Par 5	16	396	Par 4
8	183	Par 3	17	344	Par 4
9	477	Par 4	18	385	Par 4
Out	3491	Par 36	In	3180	Par 35

HOTEL INFORMATION

Hollins Hall Hotel & Country Club
Hollins Hill, Baildon, Shipley, West Yorkshire
BD17 7QW
Tel: 01274 53 00 53
Fax: 01274 53 01 87

Rooms: 122.
Restaurants: Heathcliff's restaurant (food from around the world). Long weekend Cafe Bar (informal setting).
Childcare Facilities: Creche available.
Fitness Facilities: Complimentary indoor heated swimming pool, four gyms, cardiovascular, aerobic, free weights, resistance, steam room, sauna, spa bath, activity classes, solarium, creche, heath & beauty spa.

TARIFF

DINNER, BED & BREAKFAST
(Mon-Sun)

Prices start from **£79** per person, per night, including a round of golf. Based on two sharing.

DIRECTIONS

Take junction 26 off the M62, join the M606 and take the A650 following signs to Salt's Mill. At the major traffic lights in Shipley follow the A6038 to Guiseley (straight across). Continue straight ahead for three miles and the hotel is on the left hand side. From Leeds, join the A65 to Guiseley and then the A6038. The hotel is two miles on the right hand side. Bradford and Leeds railway stations are within 10 and 20 minutes drive. Leeds/Bradford airport is also close by.

Rudding Park House & Hotel

Rudding Park House & Hotel sits in the middle of its own 2000 acre estate, just two miles south of the historic spa town of Harrogate. Over the last 25 years the Mackaness family have carefully restored the estate until it has become one of Yorkshire's finest hotel, golf and conference resorts.

LOCAL ATTRACTIONS

Being situated on the outskirts of Harrogate, just off of the A658, Rudding Park is not far away from many of Yorkshire's most famous attractions.

Castle Howard, Harewood House, Ripley Castle, Fountains Abbey and the Bronte's Parsonage are but a few local places of interest. Equally the cities of York, with the Jorvic Viking Centre and the National Railway Museum, or Leeds with the Royal Armouries and fashionable shopping centres, are close at hand. Alternatively, if a more relaxing break is sought, the Yorkshire Dales are not far away.

Voted Yorkshire's Best Hotel in 1998 by the Yorkshire Tourist Board, Rudding Park Hotel provides quality accommodation as well as the contemporary Clocktower Bar & Restaurant. The large, open stone fireplace in the reception symbolises the warm welcome for which Rudding Park is renowned. The Hotel's fifty executive bedrooms, including two suites, each offer sweeping views over the surrounding gardens, open parkland or golf course.

The Hotel is adjacent to the Regency period House which overlooks Rudding Park's 18 hole, par 72 golf course. This 6871 yard course, designed by Martin Hawtree, has become known as "Yorkshire's premier parkland course". The course has won several national environmental awards, which shows Rudding Park's deep rooted commitment to preserving and enhancing the estate's natural flora and habitats.

For guests who wish to either practise their technique or take a lesson from a Professional, Rudding Park's 18 bay floodlit covered driving range and Golf Academy is open daily to all visitors.

GOLF INFORMATION

18 hole, 6871 yard parkland course Par 72

Golf Professional: Simon Hotham

Tel: 01423 873400

Practice facilities: Covered driving range.

Instructions: Groups and individuals catered for + Academy Holes (with bunkers) and Video studio.

Hire: Clubs and buggies.

CARD OF THE COURSE					
1	393	Par 4	10	499	Par 5
2	384	Par 4	11	211	Par 3
3	463	Par 4	12	393	Par 4
4	442	Par 4	13	341	Par 4
5	164	Par 3	14	176	Par 3
6	533	Par 5	15	398	Par 4
7	456	Par 4	16	488	Par 5
8	202	Par 3	17	389	Par 4
9	525	Par 5	18	414	Par 4
Out 3562 Par 36			In 3309 Par 36		

HOTEL INFORMATION

Rudding Park House & Hotel
Rudding Park
Follifoot, Harrogate
North Yorkshire HG3 1JH
Tel: 01423 871350
Fax: 01423 872286

Rating: AA 4 Star – ETB 5 Crown highly commended.
Rooms: 50.
Restaurants: Clocktower Bar & Restaurant – Contemporary cuisine in modern surroundings + Clubhouse.
Childcare Facilities: Babysitting on request.
Fitness Facilities: Academy Health Club – 3 miles away in Harrogate offering gym, sauna and swimming pool. Tennis and beauty treatments available as extra.

TARIFF

Leisure Breaks – Single Exec. £120– Superior £140.
Double Exec. £160 – Superior £180 – Suite £250. Includes Dinner, Bed & Breakfast, complimentary newspaper, VAT + use of the Academy Club.
Special Golf Packages:
Golf breaks – include dinner, bed and breakfast, one round of golf per night stayed + basket of balls at the driving range, complimentary newspaper + VAT.
Single – Executive Room £140 – Superior Room £160.
Double – Executive Room £195 – Superior Room £215 – Suite £310.
Other Special Golf Packages:
Available on request.

DIRECTIONS

From the M1 or M62(M621) in Leeds follow the A61 Harrogate signs. At the roundabout with the A658 (Bradford/York road) take the exit for York, and follow the brown tourist signs to Rudding Park (3 miles).

DE VERE OULTON HALL

Rothwell Lane, Oulton, Leeds, West Yorkshire LS26 8HN.
Tel: 0113 2821000   Fax: 0113 2828066

18 HOLES	PAR 71	6181 YARDS

TYPE OF GOLF COURSE: Parkland

RATING: 5 Star

GOLF PROFESSIONAL: Stephen Gromett
TEL: 0113 2821000

B&B + 18 HOLES: £82.00 per person, per night.

OTHER SPECIAL GOLF PACKAGES:
£100.00 DBB per person, per night.

The only 5 star hotel in the North of England, Oulton Hall Hotel is an elegant hotel surrounded by 19th century formal gardens. The hotel has a special agreement with the adjacent Oulton Park Golf Club, venue for the De Vere PGA City of Leeds Championship in July, to guarantee guest preferential tee times. The course is as varied and as dramatic as the Yorkshire countryside that shapes and influences its challenging character.

HUNLEY HALL GOLF CLUB

Ings Lane, Brotton, Saltburn, North Yorkshire TS12 2QQ. Tel: 01287 676216 Fax: 01287 678250
Email:enquiries@hunleyhall.co.uk www.hunleyhall.com

27 HOLES	PAR 73	6918 YARDS

TYPE OF GOLF COURSE: Parkland

HOTEL RATING: 2 Star

GOLF PROFESSIONAL: Andy Brook
TEL: 01287 677444

B&B + 18 HOLES: From £48 per person

OTHER SPECIAL GOLF PACKAGES:
3 days unlimited golf, 2 nights DB&B from £150.

The club is set in over 265 acres of beautiful countryside adjoining the Heritage Coast providing a tranquil setting for all standards of golfer. 29 interchangeable holes of golf give four varied courses from a championship length 6918 yard, par 73 to a more gentle 5948 yard par 68.
The purpose built clubhouse and hotel provide a friendly atmosphere in which to relax. Two restaurants and a lounge bar offer traditional standards of service. Comfortable ensuite rooms, most with views of the course and coastline complete the facilities.

FOREST PINES HOTEL GOLF COURSE & SPA

Ermine Street, Broughton, Nr Brigg, North Lincolnshire DN20 0AQ.
Tel: 01652 650770 Fax: 01652 650495

27 HOLES	PAR 73/35	6882/3102 YARDS

TYPE OF GOLF COURSE: Undulating Wooded and open heathland setting.

HOTEL RATING: AA 3 Star + RAC 5 Crowns

DIRECTOR OF GOLF: David Edwards
TEL: 01652 650756

DINNER B&B + GOLF: 2 people sharing £83.00 per person based on two people sharing a twin/double room.

OTHER SPECIAL GOLF PACKAGES:
Golf Societies welcome

The Briggate Lodge Country Hotel lies within the grounds of Forest Pines. All 86 en-suite bedrooms are equipped with colour satellite TV, trouser press, hairdryer and direct dial telephone and recently opened leisure complex & spa. A 24 hour room service and a next day laundry service are also available.

Golf facilities include the 27 hole championship golf course and floodlit all-weather driving range. Forest Pines was recently voted the best new course in England and offers challenging play across an undulating wooded and open heathland setting.

Designed by PGA Seniors Tour player John Morgan, Forest Pines features a state of the art irrigation system, which combined with excellent drainage ensures all year round play.

LINDEN HALL HOTEL

Longhorsley, Morpeth, Northumberland, NE65 8XF. Tel: 01670 516611 Fax: 01670 788544

Linden Hall is a Grade II Listed country house hotel set in 450 acres of private wood and parkland in Mid-Northumbland, and one of the most splendid hotels in the North of England with a four-star rating. The Linden Hall Golf Club and championship length 18 hole golf course is the latest addition to the extensive facilities available which also include fifty luxurious en-suite bedrooms, a fully equipped health & leisure spa, 6 conference and banqueting suites, grounds ideal for outdoor pursuits and a choice of dining in the Dobson Restaurant or Linden Tree Bar & Grill.

18 HOLES	PAR 72	6846 YARDS

TYPE OF GOLF COURSE: Parkland

RATING: 4 Star, 5 Crown, Highly commended

GOLF PROFESSIONAL: David Curry
TEL: 01670 788050

OTHER SPECIAL GOLF PACKAGES:
One Night Residential Golf Package £79.50 per person to include 18 holes of golf, dinner (with an allowance of £15.00), overnight accommodation in one of our luxurious bedrooms and full English breakfast - Additional nights stay including all of the above £69.50 per person, additional rounds of golf £17.50 per round. NB. £20.00 per room per night single room supplement applicable.

RAMSIDE HALL HOTEL & GOLF CLUB

Carrville, Durham DH1 1TD. Tel: 0191 3865282 Fax: 0191 3860399

80 Bedrooms including premier rooms and presidential suites; 3 eating areas synonymous in the North East for over 30 years for good food at value for money prices; 2 busy 'local' bars, conference and banqueting facilities for over 700 in a variety of rooms, a magnificent golf clubhouse adjoining a driving range and surrounded by 27 holes of golf, all just 500 yards from the A1/M.

27 HOLES	PAR 36/36/34

3235/3285/2892 YARDS

TYPE OF GOLF COURSE: Parkland

RATING: AA/RAC 3 Star – 4 Crowns Highly Commended

GOLF PROFESSIONAL: Robert Lister
TEL: 0191 3869514

ALDWARK MANOR HOTEL GOLF & COUNTRY CLUB

Aldwark, Near Alne, York YO6 2NF.
Tel (Hotel): 01347 838146 (Golf Club): 01347 838333
Fax: 01347 838867

HOLES: 18	YARDS: 6171	PAR: 71

DE VERE SLALEY HALL

Hexham, Nr Newcastle Upon Tyne, Northumberland NE47 0BY.
Tel: 01434 673350 Fax: 01434 673962

HOLES: 18	YARDS: 6479	PAR: 72

HALL GARTH GOLF & COUNTRY CLUB

Coatham Mundeville, Darlington, County Durham DL1 3LU
Tel: 01325 300400 Fax: 01325 310083

HOLES: 9	YARDS: 6621	PAR: 72

Lancashire and Cumbria

Lancashire and Cumbria

*T*he Kingdom of Fife, courtesy of St Andrews, will always be the Home of Golf in the British Isles, but the capital of British golf arguably lies some 200 miles to the South.

We're talking Lancashire here, as in the Royal courses of Birkdale, Lytham & St Annes, Liverpool, as in Southport & Ainsdale, Hillside, Formby, Fairhaven, Wallasey, West Lancashire and St Annes Old Links, a truly formidable cast of great courses which you will struggle to find on any coastline anywhere in the world, let alone around the British Isles.

Twenty seven times the Open Championship has been played on this coast-line, starting at Hoylake (now Royal Liverpool) back in 1897, when amateur Harold Hilton won the championship. Hoylake staged the event 10 times before it was taken off the rota, while Royal Birkdale (8) and Royal Lytham & St Annes (9) has staged the grand old event 17 times between them.

In addition to the Open Championship, though, the Lancashire links have been host to six Ryder Cups as well as numerous amateur championships and other big events, professional and amateur.

This stretch of coastline has some of the best traditional links golf you are likely to find anywhere. Beautiful turf, towering sand dunes, pot bunkers, gorse and the most important element of all – wind.

Don't be too hung up on trying to play the big championship venues. Play them by all means, but don't miss the many hidden gems nearby. Courses like Formby, Hillside, West Lancashire and Wallasey don't quite get the same billing as their nearby neighbours, but what wonderful golf you will find there.

Don't think, though, that all of Lancashire is a series of giant sand dunes with fairways running in between. There are some good inland courses to be found in the capital of British golf. Take Pleasington, for example, or Clitheroe.

The former is a delightful parkland course near Blackburn that many rate as one of the best inland courses in the north of England. Clitheroe is another good course that sits on the edge of the Forest of Bowland. While Heswall in the Wirral is another good parkland challenge beside the River Dee that offers fine views of the far Welsh Hills.

So don't just go to the seaside when you head for Lancashire. Take a look inland as well, you're sure to be surprised.

Similarly, if you travel further up the coast into Cumbria, head for the coast and you'll find Seascale and Silloth-on-Solway. The former is an underrated links that needs to be played, even if it lies near the nuclear installation of the same name. Silloth, on the other hand is one of the best courses in the north of England, a links that is not so well known because of its remote location some 25 miles to the West of Carlisle.

Inland in Cumbria you will find the golf courses of the Lake District. Windermere, Keswick, Kendal and Penrith all provide a most pleasant day out, with views that are almost unmatched anywhere.

Lancashire and Cumbria

Page

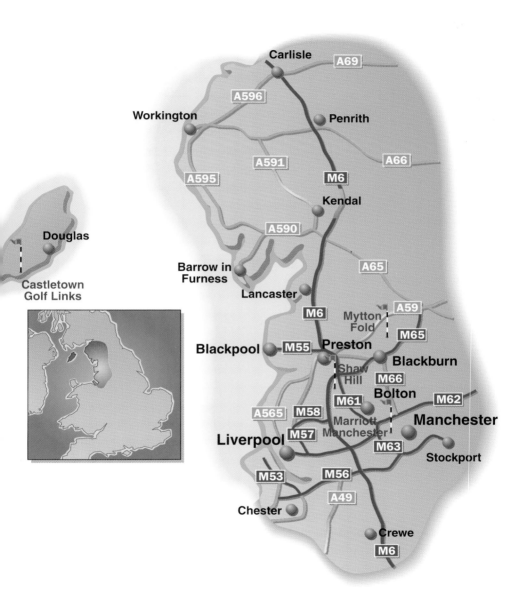

Carlisle
A69
A596
Workington
Penrith
A591
A66
A595
M6
Kendal
A590
Barrow in Furness
A65
Lancaster
M6
Mytton Fold
A59
Blackpool
M55
Preston
M65
Shaw Hill
Blackburn
Douglas
M66
Bolton
Castletown Golf Links
M61
M62
A565
M58
Marriott Manchester
Manchester
Liverpool
M57
M63
Stockport
M53
M56
A49
Crewe
Chester
M6

145

Marriott Manchester Worsley Park Hotel & Country Club

*T*he Marriott Manchester Hotel & Country Club is sited in the leafy suburb of Worsley in over 200 acres of parkland. Listed Victorian farm buildings form the basis of a £16 million development to suit all business and leisure needs.

LOCAL ATTRACTIONS

Granada Studios – television and themed visitor centre with "on set" tours.

Manchester Evening News Arena & NYNEX.

Trafford Centre – the ultimate in the indoor shopping experience with the only Selfridges outside London.

Manchester United & City FCs

Tatton Park – stately home, gardens and deer park.

Jodrell Bank – observatory and scientific centre

Close to Lake District and Yorkshire Dales.

Largest M&S in country opening late 'Nov.

The golf course offers a challenge to golfers of all abilities, requiring brains instead of brawn to make a successful score.

Try one of our stable block conversions or loft bedrooms overlooking the 1st tee and 18th green. All rooms offer minibars, trouser press, ironing centres, tea/coffee, fax/modem, satellite and guestlink TV.

Dine in the relaxing atmosphere of the Club Cafe Bar overlooking the 18th from a selection of hot and cold snacks. Alternatively, with views across to the Elizabethan Worsley Old Hall, Brindley's AA Rosette Award Winning Restaurant offers carvery buffet breakfast and lunch, turning to a la carte dining to suit all palates in the evening.

Drive out all those stress and tensions and have a work out in our 450sq metres of the latest cardio-vascular, resistance and free weights. Let our fitness instructors put you through a fitness programme designed to suit you and perhaps try one of our aerobic, yoga or step classes. Then relax in our spa bath, sauna or steam room or let our Beauty Therapists pamper you with a Decleor massage or treatment.

GOLF INFORMATION

Championship 18 hole, 6611 yard parkland/woodland course Par 71

Practice facilities: Practice ground.

Instructions: Individual and group tuition available from Head Professional David Screeton.

Hire: Trolley, Buggy, Clubs and Shoes.

CARD OF THE COURSE

1	432	Par 4	10	410	Par 4
2	371	Par 4	11	200	Par 3
3	457	Par 4	12	320	Par 4
4	184	Par 3	13	543	Par 5
5	551	Par 5	14	162	Par 3
6	544	Par 5	15	428	Par 4
7	177	Par 3	16	407	Par 4
8	422	Par 4	17	287	Par 4
9	201	Par 3	18	515	Par 5
Out	3339	Par 35	In	3272	Par 36

HOTEL INFORMATION

Marriott Manchester Worsley Park Hotel & Country Club
Worsley Park, Worsley,
Manchester M28 2QT
Tel: 0161 975 2000
Fax: 0161 799 6341
Rooms: 159.
Restaurants: Brindley's Restaurant and Club Cafe Bar.
Hair and Beauty: Health & Beauty Salon.
Other Fitness Facilities: 20 metre indoor heated pool, poolside mixed sauna, steam room and spa bath, solariums, 450sq metre cardiovascular, free weights and resistance gymnasium, fitness studio.

TARIFF

LEISURE BREAK
Mar – Apr 2000
£39.00 B&B, £59.00 DB&B

May - Sept
£44.00 B&B, £64.00 DB&B

Oct - Feb
£39.00 B&B, £59.00 DB&B

GOLF BREAK
Mar - Apr £74.00 DB&B.
May £79.00 DB&B.
June - Sept £89.00 DB&B.
Oct £79.00 DB&B.
Nov - Feb £74.00 DB&B.

Prices are per person per night. A single supplement of £30 per person per night applies.

DIRECTIONS

From the South: Take the M6 then M62 which become M60 heading towards Leeds. Exit at Junction 13 signposted Worsley. Go straight ahead at the first roundabout taking the A575 and the hotel is 400 yards on the left.
From the North: Take the M60 and exit at Junction 13. Take the fourth exit, the A572 towards Leigh. Take the third exit at the next roundabout. Follow the A575 and the hotel is 400 yards on the left.

CASTLETOWN GOLF LINKS HOTEL

Derby Haven, Isle of Man IM9 1VA. Tel: 01624 822201 Fax: 01624 824633
www.castletowngolflinks.co.uk

18 Holes	Par 72	6750 Yards

Type of Golf Course: Links

Rating: 3 Star

Golf Professional: Murray Crowe

Tel: 01634 822211

B&B + 18 Holes: From £65.00 p.p.

Family run 3 star hotel, quiet location, surrounded by the sea with stunning views. No public transport – so car recommended.

House of Manannan, Peel, Isle of Man

MYTTON FOLD HOTEL & GOLF COMPLEX
Whalley Road, Langho, Blackburn BB6 84B.
Tel: 01254 240662 Fax: 01254 248119

HOLES: 18	YARDS: 6217	PAR: 72

SHAW HILL HOTEL, GOLF & COUNTRY CLUB
Preston Road, Whittle-le-Woods, Nr Chorley, Lancs. PR6 7PP.
Tel: 01257 269221 Fax: 01257 261223

HOLES: 18	YARDS: 6239	PAR: 72

Wales

Cardiff City Hall

Wales

*I*t's taken the Welsh Tourist Board a little while, but finally they have woken up to one of their prime assets – golf.

Of course, a lot of golfers have known about the charms of Welsh golf for years. Aberdovey, Royal St David's, Royal Porthcawl, Southerdown, Tenby, Pennard, Porthmadog, Nefyn & District, Borth & Ynyslas, there are a host of good golf clubs in the province. Indeed, there are now over 170 and counting. For a long time there was just over 100, but a building boom has taken place that has seen golf become an ever increasing use of Welsh leisure time.

The Welsh Tourist Board has realised what has been under their nose for so long and is now pushing golf as part of its campaign to attract visitors to the country.

There are a number of attractions to travelling to Wales rather than some of the other more well known golf destinations in the British Isles. For a start it's still not a hugely popular place for golfers to visit, meaning you can usually get a game even in mid-summer. Secondly it is fairly easy to get to from most parts of the UK. Thirdly it has a host of hotels and B & Bs where the welcome is genuine and the prices won't break the bank.

Golfers travelling to Wales are advised to travel the entire coastline – from North to South or South to North, depending where you hail from – to get a true sample of the golf on offer. Okay, so you might not make it in one trip. Fine, it just means you'll have to go back. Pity.

Let's start in the South, if only because the jewel of Welsh golf lies there.

Royal Porthcawl is the gem on offer, a links course that has hosted numerous championships over the years. For example, it was venue for the 1995 Walker Cup, when Great Britain & Ireland defeated an American side that contained Tiger Woods. That Woods was not able to master the Porthcawl links should tell you that it isn't a course to be toyed with.

Porthcawl isn't blessed with the towering sand dunes typical of some links courses. Nor do the fairways seem to ripple and roll as they do on other traditional links. In fact, looking at it from the clubhouse, it looks fairly tame. It isn't. The absence of huge dunes means every hole at Porthcawl is exposed, so that when the wind blows it sweeps over the entire course. As the American Walker Cup team found to their horror, this is links to be treated with respect.

That's fairly typical of links golf in Wales. Aberdovey is another links course you must respect if you are to play, especially on a wild day. Wedged between the sea and the railway line, typical of Old Prestwick, Aberdovey nestles on perfect links terrain. So perfect that Bernard Darwin, the grandfather of golf writing, called it his favourite course in the world. Some claim, and one you may agree with after playing it. And if you discount old Darwin, then maybe this will spur you to pay this grand old course a visit: Ian Woosnam is an honorary member and regular visitor.

Further up the coast, in North Wales, you will find the third of the great trio of Welsh links golf – Royal St David's at Harlech. Lying in the shadow of Harlech Castle and within sight of Mount Snowdon are the Harlech links, where golf has been played since 1894.

While the card may only read par-69 on a course that measures less than 6,500 yards, by common consent St David's plays a lot longer. To give you a clue, the standard scratch score is 72. In other words don't be complacent when you take on St David's.

Aberdovey, Royal Porthcawl, Royal St David's these are the highlights of Welsh golf. Luckily there are no real lowlights, just plenty of hidden gems waiting to explored.

And if you're looking for golf of the inland variety, then the new Celtic Manor course at Newport is worth checking out. There's a hotel there and two Robert Trent Jones designed courses that have been built to impeccable standards. Or there's St Pierre, now owned by the Marriott hotel group, where a European Tour event used to be held. Or you might want to try the Rolls of Monmouth in the Wye Valley; just the name is tempting enough.

Or maybe you'll just want to explore, for Wales has numerous courses, some just delightful nine holers just waiting to be found.

Wales

Page

Henlly's Hall
Colwyn Bay
Bangor
A55
Bryn Morfydd Golf Hotel
Caernarfon
Wrexham
A487
A5
A494
A470
Oswestry
A5
Shrewsbury
Dogellau
Welshpool
M50
Aberystwyth
A49
A470
A487
Builth Wells
Hereford
Fishguard
Carmarthen
M50
Haverfordwest
A40
A48
A40
A465
A48
Merthyr Tydfil
Ross-on-wye
Milford Haven
Llanelli
Neath
St Mary's Hotel
Celtic Manor Hotel
Marriott St Pierre Hotel
Swansea
Pontypridd
Newport
M4
Cardiff
A48

Marriott St Pierre Hotel & Country Club

*T*he Marriott St. Pierre Hotel & Country Club is set in 400 acres of picturesque parkland in the beautiful Wye Valley. London is only a couple of hours away and Birmingham even less.

The hotel has over 140 bedrooms (including 16 suites), each one of them enjoying a most scenic view.

LOCAL ATTRACTIONS

St Pierre occupies a corner of the country with more than its fair share of attractions, such as the beauty of the Wye Valley, historic sights – from Tintern Abbey to the impressive Roman remains at Bath, as well as the famous Stuart Crystal works.

The Executive Chef has worked in the kitchens of the world's most famous hotels. Using the best local produce, such as freshly caught River Wye salmon and tender Welsh lamb, he has created a tempting variety of imaginative dishes for all tastes. The newly refurbished Long Weekend Café Bar offers a light hearted informal sports theme restaurant, and room service is available 24 hours a day.

You'll find plenty of ways either to wind yourself down or tone yourself up at the Marriott St. Pierre. The hotel has extensive health and beauty facilities, including a beauty suite with five treatment rooms, offering everything from a manicure to a full body massage.

If you're seeking more active relaxation, St. Pierre can offer a wealth of activities, including tennis, multi-gymnasium, aerobic suite, cycling and even hot air ballooning.

GOLF INFORMATION

Old Course, 6818 yards, Par 71, 18-hole. Mathern Course, 5732 yards, Par 68, 18-hole, heathland/woodland course.

Practice facilities: Putting green and driving range.

Instructions: Groups and individuals catered for. Tuition and Video facilities.

Hire: Clubs & equipment, trollies and buggies.

CARD OF THE COURSE
Old Course White Tees

1	576	Par 5	10	371	Par 4
2	365	Par 4	11	393	Par 4
3	168	Par 3	12	550	Par 5
4	379	Par 4	13	219	Par 3
5	420	Par 4	14	521	Par 5
6	165	Par 3	15	375	Par 4
7	442	Par 4	16	453	Par 4
8	309	Par 4	17	449	Par 4
9	444	Par 4	18	237	Par 3
Out	3235	Par 35	In	3527	Par 36

MONMOUTHSHIRE

HOTEL INFORMATION

Marriott St. Pierre Hotel & Country Club
St. Pierre Park,
Chepstow NP16 6YA
Tel: 01291 625261
Fax: 01291 629975

Rooms: 148.
Restaurants: Orangery Restaurant, Long Weekend Café Bar, Trophy Bar.
Hair and Beauty: Health spa including five treatment rooms.
Other Fitness Facilities: Indoor heated swimming pool, spa bath, sauna, gym, solarium.
Other Sporting Facilities: Tennis courts, dance studiofree weights room.

TARIFF

DINNER, BED & BREAKFAST
(Mon-Sun)

Prices start from **£94** per person, per night, including a round of golf on either course. Based on two sharing.

DIRECTIONS

Take Junction 21 off the M4 sign-posted M48 Chepstow. Then take Junction 2 off the M48 and follow the A466 sign-posted Chepstow. At the first roundabout turn left onto the A48 towards Caerwent. Marriott St. Pierre is approximately 2 miles on the left.

157

THE CELTIC MANOR RESORT

Catsash Road, Newport, Gwent NP18 1HQ. Tel: 01633 413000 Fax: 01633 412910

54 HOLES   PAR 59/69/70
4001/6700/7403 YARDS
TYPE OF GOLF COURSE: Parkland
RATING: AA/RAC/WTB 5 Star
GOLF PROFESSIONAL: Chris Baron
TEL: 01633 410311
B&B + 18 HOLES: £99 (½ twin, incl dinner)
OTHER SPECIAL GOLF PACKAGES:
Contact golf reservations 01633 413000

The Celtic Manor Court Resort. 3 challenging, very different Trent Jones Championship Courses. Luxury 400 room, 32 suite hotel, 1500 delegate Convention Centre, 35 function rooms, 4 restaurants, 2 outstanding Health Clubs & Spa; Ian Woosnam Golf Academy; Tennis. Wentwood Hills (7403 yd par 72) home of 'Welsh Open' with Ryder Cup ambitions, 'a jewel' say European Tour; Roman Road voted Wales' best inland course; Coldra Woods PGA short course championship venue. Stunning panoramas. Luxurious Clubhouse visitor facilities, Health Club, Lounge Bar and Dining Terrace; banqueting.

Trearddur Bay, Isle of Anglesey

BRYN MORFYDD HOTEL

Lanrhaeadr, Nr. Denbigh, Benbighshire LL16 4NP.
Tel: 01745 890280 Fax: 01745 890488

HOLES: 9/18   **YARDS:** 2000/5800 **PAR:** 27/70

HENLLY'S HALL HOTEL

Beaumaris, Isle of Anglesey, North Wales
Tel: 01248 810412 Fax: 01248 811511

HOLES: 18   **YARDS:** 6062   **PAR:** 72

ST. MARY'S HOTEL GOLF & COUNTRY CLUB (BEST WESTERN)

St. Mary's Hill, Pencoed, South Glamorgan CF35 5WA.
Tel: 01656 861100/860280 Fax: 01656 863400

HOLES: 9/18 **YARDS:** 2426/5291 **PAR:** 35/69

Western Scotland

Kilchurn Castle, Loch Awe

Western Scotland

Not many people venture further down the Ayrshire coast beyond Turnberry. They come to play the famous Ailsa course, where the Open Championship has been staged three times, perhaps stay in the magnificent hotel, and then head for home. That's a pity.

Further down the coastline, down in Dumfries and Galloway, are to be found some surprisingly good golf courses. Portpatrick, Stranraer, Powfoot, Dumfries & County, there are plenty of hidden gems to keep you happy. Best of the bunch, though, is Southerness. This is a links golf par excellence that does not get the publicity it deserves because it is perceived to be off the beaten track, as if it was stuck out in the middle of the wild Atlantic Ocean or something. Any aficionado of links golf needs to put this 6,566-yard course on their must play list. It will not disappoint.

Nor will golf in the nearby Borders region disappoint. This area is too often bypassed by golfers hurrying towards Glasgow or Edinburgh, yet it contains a host of parkland gems well worth stopping for – Minto, Hawick, The newly opened Roxburghe, Selkirk, St. Boswells, all worthy of a round.

But it's to the giants of the Ayrshire coast that we are headed, and there is no bigger than Turnberry or Royal Troon.

Troon is the tougher of the two, especially over the closing nine, while Turnberry is more picturesque. To play them on consecutive days is to experience the twin peaks of Ayrshire golf.

Of course, with the boom in golf came more desire to play these courses, and both are hard to get on to. Troon especially does not accept too many visitors, so, like many Open venues, perseverance is required. Turnberry is more straightforward. By staying at the hotel you gain playing privileges on the course, although you do pay extra for the green fee. That's obviously a costly option as the hotel is five star throughout. However, in winter the hotel offers some good deals, and that may be your best option. It's a viable option, too, for this coastline is warmed by the Gulfstream and can be quite temperate in winter compared to the rest of Scotland.

If you can't beg, steal or borrow a round over these two famous links then don't despair too much – there are enough quality venues nearby to keep you happy. Glasgow Gailes, Kilmarnock Barassie, Irvine Bogside, Western Gailes, all Open Qualifying courses, are not too far away from Troon. All provide a great challenge and a good day's golf.

The same can be said of Old Prestwick, where the Open Championship began in

1860. Anyone remotely interested in the history of the game has to try to play here. Of course it's too short nowadays to challenge the top players, but not short enough for the top amateurs or your game either, especially if the wind blows.

As you would expect, there's good public golf to be found in this area. For example, the courses of Lochgreen, Darley and Fullarton are all good links layouts in their own rights. True, they may not be as manicured as some of the aforementioned layouts, but they offer good challenges and even better value for money. They do get quite busy in the summer so make sure you phone ahead. And don't worry about teaming up with a local; often you find yourself playing with someone who appears to be a few strokes better than his handicap. They take their golf quite seriously up here!

They take the "goff" quite seriously around Glasgow, too. No longer is Glasgow the grimy industrial city it once was. It's not too long ago that it was voted the European city of Culture, an honour it still lives up to admirably.

With close to 100 golf courses in and around the city, you're never short of a game.

South of the city try Lanark Golf Club, a moorland course that Old Tom Morris, Ben Sayers and James Braid have had a hand in creating – a trio to make most other clubs jealous. The R & A rate the Lanark layout so highly that it has been used as a regular course for Open Qualifying.

Closer to the city, you are not spoilt for choice. Haggs Castle should be at the top of your list. This fine parkland layout was venue for the now defunct Scottish Open in its inaugural year of 1986. Other courses in or near the city to consider include the James Braid designed Hilton Park, Glasgow Killermont, Renfrew and East Renfrew.

North of the city you might try Helensburgh, Cardross, the short but hilly Vale of Leven, a course offering tremendous views over Loch Lomond, and Buchanan Castle.

If you have lots of time on your hands, and you don't mind the three hour drive, then you should try and get to Machrihanish. How good is Machrihanish? Well, just prior to the 1994 Open Championship, American Ryder Cup player Brad Faxon drove round from Turnberry to play this testing links course. Faxon didn't seem to mind the long drive or the fact he had to have a catnap in his car.

The trip is worth it for Machrihanish, as Old Tom Morris said when asked to design it in 1879, was "specially designed by the Almighty for playing golf." That applies today. Just to play the opening hole is worth the effort. And if you can throw in a round at The Machrie over the water on Islay, then you will have played two of the most natural links in the world.

Western Scotland

Page

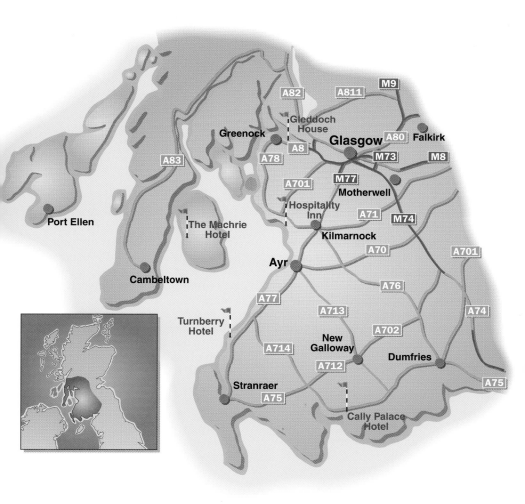

165

Cally Palace Hotel

The Cally Palace Hotel in South West Scotland stands in its own grounds at the edge of the village of Gatehouse-of-Fleet. The house was built in 1763 and many original features remain. It is four star and deluxe in every respect, but with an ambience which is both elegant and formal yet warm and friendly.

LOCAL ATTRACTIONS

In the surrounding area there are lovely gardens and castles to visit and the hotel is just a few miles from the sea. Castles include Threave, Drumlanrig and gardens range from Castle Kennedy to the botanical Logan Gardens heading towards Stranraer.

The 18 hole golf course is 5800 yards with a par of 70 and is set in lovely rolling parkland and around Cally Lake. It is for the exclusive use of Hotel guests – no members, no day visitors and no competitions.

The 56 bedrooms are made up of standard, family, deluxe rooms and suites, most with delightful views of the grounds or across Cally Lake to the Galloway Hills. The food is absolutely first class under the guidance of Head Chef David Alexander whose innovative style of cooking is very popular with regular guests and those visiting for the first time. In particular he makes best use of locally caught seafood and game, and of course Scottish Beef regularly appears on his menus.

Indoor leisure facilities include swimming pool, sauna, jacuzzi and guests who enjoy the outdoor life will appreciate the 500 acres of grounds surrounding the hotel – for walking or boating on the lake. Salmon fishing, archery and pony trekking can all be arranged nearby.

GOLF INFORMATION

18 hole, 5802 yard parkland course

Par 70

Hire: buggies

CARD OF THE COURSE					
1	287	Par 4	10	361	Par 4
2	165	Par 3	11	339	Par 4
3	381	Par 4	12	172	Par 3
4	335	Par 4	13	401	Par 4
5	378	Par 4	14	266	Par 4
6	128	Par 3	15	504	Par 5
7	332	Par 4	16	345	Par 4
8	579	Par 5	17	221	Par 3
9	337	Par 4	18	271	Par 4
Out	2922	Par 35	In	2880	Par 35

HOTEL INFORMATION

Cally Palace Hotel
Gatehouse-of-Fleet,
Castle Douglas,
Dumfries & Galloway
DG7 2DL
Tel: 01557 814341
Fax: 01557 814 522
Rating: AA + RAC 4 Star, AA Rosette for
food, STB four Star.
Rooms: 56.
Restaurants: Scottish – using local
produce.
Childcare Facilities: Baby listening service.
Other Fitness Facilities: 2 exercise bikes.
Other Sporting Facilites: Tennis court,
croquet, putting and indoor swimming pool.

TARIFF

Weekend Breaks
from £164pp for 2
nights DBB & Golf.

**Mid-Week Breaks
(Min Stay 2 nights)**
from £82pppn DBB & Golf.
Over 60's Reduction.

Weekly golf rates
from £81pppn DBB & Golf.

DIRECTIONS

Head north on the M6 and
cross onto the A75 heading
towards Dumfries/Stranraer.
Alternatively head south on
the A74 from Glasgow and
then turn off on to the A75
following signs for Dumfries. Once at
Dumfries follow A75 towards
Stranraer. Approximately 15 miles west
of Castle Douglas take the first right
onto the B727 following signs for
Gatehouse-of-Fleet – the Hotel is on
the left before Gatehouse.

Gleddoch House Hotel

Gleddoch House and its 360 acre estate was once the home of shipping Baron, Sir James Lithgrow. Gleddoch is the ideal base from which to explore Scotland's famous sights and attractions, uniquely situated 10 minutes from Glasgow Airport and 20 minutes from City Centre.

All of the bedrooms have en-suite facilities,

each has its own individual character, offering picturesque views of the gardens and surrounding estate. The garden restaurant has achieved international recognition for its high standard of cuisine, prepared by our award winning chef.

We offer an impressive selection of indoor and outdoor activities. Our 18 hole par 71 Golf Course, with its surrounding estate provides a unique challenge to all Golfers.

Outdoor sports enthusiasts can enjoy the challenge of our organised clay-pigeon shoots, or experience the excitement and exhilaration of off-road adventure driving. The Equestrian Centre offers guests of all ages and abilities the opportunity to explore the wealth of attractions throughout the estate.

For a more relaxing experience, enjoy a picturesque walk through our formal gardens and ramble over the surrounding scenic countryside.

Our conference facilities comprise of five stylish, magnificently appointed rooms which can be used for meetings, product launches and seminars, as well as conferences for up to 120 delegates.

LOCAL ATTRACTIONS

Gleddoch House offers the best of both world's set in the peace and tranquillity of the rolling Renfrewshire hills, yet only ten minutes from Glasgow Airport, and Twenty minutes from the City Centre.

GOLF INFORMATION

18 hole, 6335 yard Parkland/Moorland course Par 68

Golf Professional: Keith Campbell
Tel: 01475 540711

Instructions: Groups and individuals catered for.

Hire: Clubs and buggies

Green Fees: Week day – £30.00 Per round, £40.00 full day. Weekends – £40.00 per round. £50.00 full day. Residents are entitled to 50% discount on above fees.

CARD OF THE COURSE

1	319	Par 4	10	314	Par 4
2	181	Par 3	11	524	Par 5
3	517	Par 4	12	172	Par 3
4	389	Par 4	13	496	Par 5
5	438	Par 4	14	185	Par 3
6	408	Par 4	15	372	Par 4
7	145	Par 3	16	396	Par 4
8	270	Par 4	17	423	Par 4
9	341	Par 4	18	393	Par 4
Out	3008	Par 35	In	3275	Par 36

HOTEL INFORMATION

Gleddoch House Hotel, Langbank, Renfrewshire, PA14 6YE
Tel: 0147 5540711
Fax: 01475 540201
Rating: AA 4 Star, 2 AA Rosettes, RAC 4 Star, STB – 4 Star
Rooms: 39.
Restaurants: AA 2 Rossettes awarded restaurant.
Other Sporting Facilities: Clay pigeon shooting, archery, Equestrian centre.
Other Leisure Activities: Off road driving.

TARIFF

Package one:
One day package (Sat-Sun), breakfast, two rounds of golf, lunch, dinner. £70.00 per person

Package two:
One day package (Sat-Sun) B&B, two rounds of golf, lunch dinner, £125.00 per person.

Package three:
Two day package (Fri,Sat,Sun) B&B, four rounds of golf, lunch dinner, £150.00 per person.

DIRECTIONS

From Glasgow (and/or Airport) take the M8 (Greenock direction) and take the B789 Langbank/Houston exit. Follow the signs to the left and then right after 1/2 mile, the hotel driveway is signed on the left.

RENFREWSHIRE

1
169

Machrie Hotel & Golf Links

The Machrie hotel was originally built about 250 years ago as a farmhouse. Nowadays it has 16 en-suite bedrooms, including a suite and a four poster. All rooms have colour TV, direct dial telephone and tea making facilities. There are also 15 two bedroom lodges sleeping between 4-6 which provide even more privacy and freedom and are fully equipped for self catering purposes. The lodges are also available for groups of golfers on a fully inclusive golf package. The island abounds in local beef and lamb, game, venison and shellfish and these feature widely on our menu. A Scottish base complemented by dishes with an international essence ensure a wide variety of choice of food cooked to perfection. We also have a private dining room seating up to 40 people should your group wish for a more intimate dinner. Settle down after dinner in front of a peat fire and savour one of the island's eight malts or if you are feeling more energetic why not try your hand at snooker, pool, table tennis or one of the other indoor sports on offer. The golf course laid out in 1891 by Willie Campbell has changed little since that time. Sand dunes provide natural hazards but will challenge most golfers and the blind shots make for an interesting first round. This is a course that takes you back in time to how golf used to be played. It is the golfer against nature and the challenge is to see who wins! Our aim is to ensure that everybody who comes to Machrie has the chance to play a challenging course, eat wonderful food and relax in the friendly atmosphere of the hotel and the island.

LOCAL ATTRACTIONS

The island is most famous for its malt whisky, which has a distinctive peaty flavour. There are 6 operational distilleries, four of which are very close to the hotel and we can arrange tours for you. Horse riding, stalking, fishing and birdwatching are some of the most popular sports on Islay, which is renowned for its extensive variety of bird life including geese, hen harriers and golden eagles. The Woollen Mill is a popular attraction with two spinning Jennies and the only Slubbing Billy in the country. The main attraction of the island is the peace and beauty and its numerous golden beaches, ideal for water sports or just relaxing.

GOLF INFORMATION

18 hole, 6226 yard links course

Par 71

Practice facilities: Outdoor driving range.

Hire: Clubs and Trollies.

CARD OF THE COURSE					
1	308	Par 4	10	156	Par 3
2	508	Par 5	11	357	Par 4
3	319	Par 4	12	174	Par 3
4	390	Par 4	13	488	Par 5
5	163	Par 3	14	423	Par 4
6	344	Par 4	15	335	Par 4
7	395	Par 4	16	411	Par 4
8	337	Par 4	17	352	Par 4
9	392	Par 4	18	374	Par 4
Out 3156 Par 36			In 3070 Par 35		

HOTEL INFORMATION

Machrie Hotel & Golf Links
Port Ellen, Isle of Islay
Argyll PA42 7AN
Tel: 01496 302310
Fax: 01496 302404
E-mail: machrie@machrie.com
Rating: 3 Star Scottish Tourist Board.
Rooms: 16 plus 15 two bedroomed lodges.
Restaurants: Scottish using local game and shellfish. Private dining room.
Childcare Facilities: Babysitting can be arranged. Childrens play area.
Hair and Beauty: Hairdressing salon in hotel - aromatherapy can be arranged.
Other Sporting Facilities: Croquet lawn, snooker, pool table, table tennis, darts, carpet bowls, bike hire, fishing, nature trail.

TARIFF

Golfing Breaks
March/Oct – £65.00
May/Sept – £80.00
Nov/Feb – £55.00
April – £75.00

All prices per person per night.

Golf Rates:
B&B from £37.00. Golf £22.50/rn.

DIRECTIONS

Ferry from Kennacraig to Port Ellen/Port Askaig. Take A846 from ferry. Scheduled air service twice daily from Glasgow. Free transfers to and from both ferry and airport can be arranged.

Ayr, South Ayrs

THISTLE HOTEL, IRVINE

46 Annick Road, Irvine KA11 4LD. Tel: 01294 274 272 Fax: 01294 277 287 Email: irvine@thistle.co.uk

Recently refurbished to a very high standard, the hotel is ideally situated for the 34 golf courses in the area. Facilities include 2 bars, Mirage Restaurant. Tropical Hawaiian Lagoon with Restaurant, Extensive beer garden and childrens play area. Conference facilities. Visit Thistle Hotels website or www.thistlehotels.com

9 HOLES	PAR 27	1485 YARDS

TYPE OF GOLF COURSE: Parkland

RATING: 4 Star AA/RAC

GOLF PROFESSIONAL: Bill Lockie (Associate) (contact through hotel)

SPECIAL PACKAGES: available includinglocal golf. excellent group rates.

TURNBERRY HOTEL

Turnberry, Ayrshire KA26 9LT. Tel: 01655 331000 Fax: 01655 331706

Turnberry Hotel is located on the West Coast of Scotland approximately one hour from Glasgow. The Hotel has 132 guest bedrooms including 21 suites and studio suites, three restaurants and four bars. The Ailsa course, host to three Open Championships in 1977, 1986 and 1994 will be partnered by the equally challenging New Arran course opening spring 2001.

In addition to golf, the Hotel also has one of the country's finest health spa's with a range of up to 25

18/18 HOLES PAR 70/68	6976/6014 YARDS

TYPE OF GOLF COURSE: Links courses

HOTEL RATING: AA 5 Red Stars/RAC 5 Star Blue Ribbon/STB 5 Crowns Deluxe

GOLF PROFESSIONAL: Brian Gunson
TEL: 01655 331000

B&B + 18 HOLES: From £145.00

different treatments which include aromatherapy, hydrotherapy, mud and algae wraps. A beauty salon is also available together with gift shops and a golf professional shop in the Clubhouse and the new Colin Montgomerie Links Golf Academy.

Eastern Scotland

Stonehaven Harbour, Grampian

Eastern Scotland

Y ou can't call yourself a true golfer if you haven't played golf in The Kingdom. We're talking Fife here, as in St Andrews, the home of golf. Every year thousands of visitors roll into St Andrews to play the Old Course, where the game began. It's a pilgrimage every golfer should make at least once, but many play St Andrews and then move on to other Open venues. Not that the likes of Turnberry and Royal Troon are to be sneezed at, but golf in Fife stretches farther than the Old Course – a lot farther.

Think of it. Where else will you find a better stretch of golf than the likes of Leven Links, Lundin Links, Elie, Crail, Scotscraig on the coast, and Ladybank in the heart of the Kingdom? Indeed, you could spend a week playing golf in Fife without going to St Andrews and still have a great experience, so good is the golf on offer. You could even have a good time if you play golf in the "auld grey toon" but don't happen to be lucky enough to get drawn from the ballot to play the Old Course. The New Course is not a bad stand-in for the old lady of golf. And the Eden and Jubilee courses are not to be snee zed at either. Neither is the new Duke's course at Craigtoun. A demanding layout which is the property of the Old Course hotel. This parkland course is built to excellent specifications and offers good views over the town and its most famous assets.

Great golf is to be found if you head over the Tay Bridge to Tayside, or over the Forth Road Bridge south to the Lothians.

For example, in Tayside there is arguably the toughest of the current Open Championship courses – Carnoustie, to the north of Dundee. This demanding links hosted the Open Championship in 1999, 24 years after Tom Watson won his first of five Old Claret Jugs in a playoff with Australia's Jack Newton in 1975.

Although you cannot view the sea from Carnoustie's fairways, this is a true links course in every sense of the word. It's a giant of a links too. The finish is arguably the toughest on the Open rota. Any player with the lead through 14 holes should not start preparing his victory speech, for the next four holes could send him hurtling back down through the field.

Good links golf in this area can also be found at Panmure, Monifieth and Montrose. Panmure is fairly short at just over 6,300 yards to a par of 70, but it's tight and tough and demands attention if you're to match your handicap. The legendary Ben Hogan was suitably impressed with this course when qualifying for the 1953 Open, which he won.

Both Monifieth and Montrose, further up the coast, are public links courses, so the green fee won't stretch your wallet, but the courses will, especially in a strong sea breeze.

Don't think golf in Tayside is just a collection of good links courses. There are also fine inland courses within striking distance of the city of Dundee. Downfield, Edzell, Letham Grange, all provide a welcome change from the seaside. Even further inland, towards the heart of Scotland, there is good golf to be found at Blairgowrie, at Pitlochry, at Crieff, at Murrayshall. Blairgowrie, for instance, is one of Scotland's true hidden gems, a club often missed on many itineraries for some strange reason. Yet the Rosemount course there is a joy to behold – heather, gorse, pine and silver birch trees and fine moorland fairways complete a fabulous picture.

All that's to the north of the Kingdom, to the south is yet another centre of great golf, where there are enough good links to keep you happy for a fortnight.

The centre is Gullane. Of course, the Open Championship rolls into this small town every five or so years. It comes to Muirfield, where the Honourable Company of Edinburgh golfers, the world's oldest golf club, are based.

Getting on to Muirfield is about as easy these days as getting an audience with the Prime Minister – in fact it's probably easier to see the PM! – so it might be a while before you sample its famous fairways. Fear not though, for almost literally within par-5 distance are a host of good courses.

Gullane has three courses and there are many who rate the Number 1 course as one of the best links in the country. Many also rate Luffness New which is also to be found in the town. Indeed, the R & A rate it highly enough to have held Open Qualifying over its links.

Not far from Gullane are to be found other fine links courses at Longniddry, Kilspindie, North Berwick and Dunbar. Indeed, the West Links at North Berwick is home to the famous Redan hole, the 15th, which has been copied on other courses all over the world.

Of course if you're in the Lothians then you will no doubt visit Edinburgh, the Athens of the North. The sights are what you will be going to see but don't forget your clubs. Around Edinburgh you will find good golf at Bruntsfield Links, Royal Burgess, Braid Hills, Dalmahoy and Royal Musselburgh, to name but a few. Some of these layouts are difficult to play and so a little advance planning is required. One thing's for sure – it will be worth the effort.

Eastern Scotland

Page

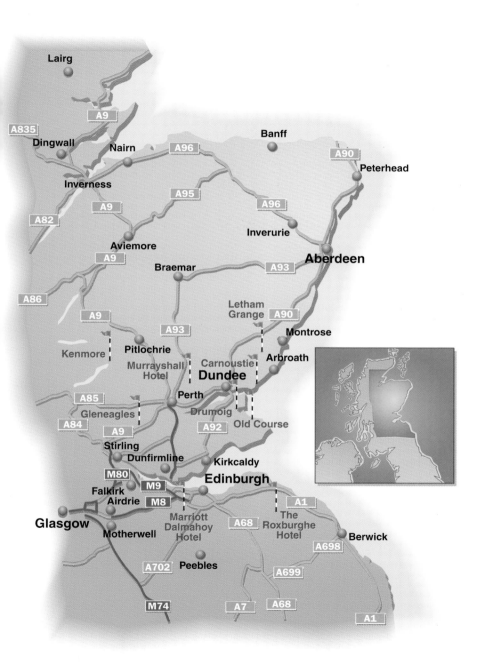

Lairg

A9

A835

Dingwall   Nairn   A96   Banff   A90

Inverness   A95   A96   Peterhead

A82   A9   Inverurie

Aviemore   A93   Aberdeen
A9
Braemar

A86   Letham
Grange   A90
A9   Montrose
A93
Kenmore   Pitlochrie
Murrayshall   Carnoustie   Arbroath
Hotel   Dundee
A85   Perth
Gleneagles   Drumoig
A84   A9   A92   Old Course
Stirling
Dunfirmline   Kirkcaldy
M80
Falkirk   M9   Edinburgh
Airdrie   M8   A1
Glasgow   Marriott
Dalmahoy   A68   The
Hotel   Roxburghe   Berwick
Motherwell   Hotel   A698
A702   Peebles   A699
M74   A7   A68
A1

179

Carnoustie Hotel, Golf Resort & Spa

You will walk in the footsteps of champions when you visit Carnoustie Hotel, Golf Resort and Spa, one of only two venues in Britain that can offer hotel guests guaranteed tee times on an Open Championship golf course.

Described by the great Gary Player as "probably the toughest golf course in the world" when he won The Open there in 1968, the Championship Course at Carnoustie is recognised throughout the world as being one of the most challenging and thrilling tests of golf.

And for the ultimate in convenience, the excellent Pro Shop and expansive locker rooms are located on the ground floor of the hotel, only a few steps away from the first tee and the 18th green.

In addition to Carnoustie's other two courses the Burnside and Buddon Links, there is also an amazing choice of other great golf courses to play in the area.

The luxurious new hotel has 85 well appointed bedrooms and suites, many of which have superb views over the course and the eastern seaboard.

Sample great food from Scotland's larder, served with Mediterranean flair in the splendid Dalhousie Restaurant overlooking the 18th green or enjoy more informal dishes in Calder's Bar or on the Terrace.

Non golfers are also well catered for. The Spa is a perfect haven for rejuvenation and relaxation with its large swimming pool, sauna, steam room, whirlpool, gym and treatment rooms.

LOCAL ATTRACTIONS

Within a short drive of Carnoustie there is so much to see and do - you can visit historical castles such as Glamis, famous old whisky distilleries like Glenturret, the attractive fishing villages of the east coast, or just enjoy the magnificent scenery. The towns of Dundee, Perth and St Andrews are also within easy reach.

GOLF INFORMATION

18 hole, 6941 yard Links

Par 72

Golf Professional: Willie Milne
Tel: 01241 411999

Practice facilities: Extensive practice putting green.

Instructions: Groups and individuals catered for.

Hire: Sets of clubs and shoes available.

CARD OF THE COURSE

1	401	Par 4	10	446	Par 4
2	435	Par 4	11	362	Par 4
3	337	Par 4	12	479	Par 5
4	375	Par 4	13	161	Par 3
5	387	Par 4	14	483	Par 5
6	520	Par 5	15	459	Par 4
7	394	Par 4	16	245	Par 3
8	167	Par 3	17	433	Par 4
9	413	Par 4	18	444	Par 4
Out	3429	Par 36	In	3512	Par 36

HOTEL INFORMATION

Carnoustie Hotel, Golf Resort & Spa, The Links, Carnoustie. DD7 7JE Scotland
Tel: 01241411999
Fax: 01241 411998
Rating: AA 4 Star.
Rooms: 85.
Restaurants: Dalhousie Restaurant - fine dining; Calders Bar & Terrace - informal
Childcare Facilities: Babysitting can be arranged.
Hair & Beauty Facilities: Hair dressing & beauty treatments available.
Fitness Facilities: Spa with large swimming pool, sauna, steam room, whirlpool. Fully equipped gym treatment rooms.
Other Sporting Facilites: Riding, hunting, shooting & fishing nearby.

TARIFF

Dinner,Bed & Breakfast + 18 holes on The Championship Course
Prices are per person per night, based on two sharing.

April - October: From £165.00.
November - March: From £105.00.

Visit www.carnoustie-hotel.com for details of special offers.

DIRECTIONS

From Glasgow and the west via A9, A90 to Dundee then follow signs to Carnoustie via A92.

From Edinburgh and the south: via Forth Road Bridge, M90, A90 to Dundee, then follow signs to Carnoustie via A92.

Drumoig Hotel & Golf Course

*D*rumoig Golf Resort (near St Andrews) is Scotland's exciting new Golf location, with it's own 18 hole championship golf course and a unique lodge-hotel and clubhouse arrangement offering the golfer a relaxed environment. All rooms are en-suite with satellite TV, tea & coffee making facilities. 5 Executive Whisky Trail Suites are located in the main building.

LOCAL ATTRACTIONS

There are many exciting attractions all within easy driving distance, including; Sea Life, Crieff, Secret Bunker, Edinburgh Zoo, The Great Houses of Scotland, British Golf Museum, Praytis Farm Park, The Glenturret, Rankeilout Park, as well as Whisky distilleries, The Mill Trail, The Whisky Trail all surround by spectacular landscapes.

Drumoig is Home to the Scottish National Golf Centre - the UK's finest indoor and outdoor training and practice facility attracting golfers from throughout the world.

Drumoig's golf layout is wholly natural over sand based ground in rolling terrain. Links-like in parts with two greens nestling in the old whinstone quarries, water also plays an intrinsic part with three holes adjoining the somewhat intimidating lochs. The views are spectacular with St Andrews Bay and town seen to the south and Carnoustie to the north-east.

The superb new Clubhouse with it's restaurant and terrace provides outstanding views over the 9th and 18th greens and imposing water features beyond. A perfect setting to enjoy relaxing drinks or a meal in the bar or restaurant. During the day we offer a specially prepared menu for the golfer or visitor on the move. In the evening the pace relaxes to allow the option of à la carte dining with a Scottish and International flavour.

GOLF INFORMATION

18 hole, 7006 yard Rolling links style – inland course
Par 72

Golf Professional: on site.

Practice facilities: Covered driving range.

Instructions: Groups and individuals catered for. Drumoig is the Home of The Scottish National Golf Centre.

Hire: Clubs, trolleys and buggies.

CARD OF THE COURSE

1	432	Par 4	10	396	Par 4
2	218	Par 3	11	340	Par 4
3	563	Par 5	12	422	Par 4
4	214	Par 3	13	300	Par 4
5	565	Par 5	14	202	Par 3
6	430	Par 4	15	582	Par 5
7	379	Par 4	16	190	Par 3
8	358	Par 4	17	539	Par 5
9	434	Par 4	18	442	Par 4
Out	3593	Par 36	In	3413	Par 36

HOTEL INFORMATION

Drumoig Hotel & Golf Course
St Andrews, Fife KY16 0BE
Tel: 01382 541800
Fax: 01382 542211
www: www.drumoigleisure.com
email: drumoig@sol.co.uk

Rating: STB 3 stars, AA 3 stars.
Rooms: 29 = 18 Twin, 6 Double and 5 Executive Whisky Trail Suites.
Restaurants: Snacks, Bar Meals, à la Carte, Scottish and International cuisine.
Fitness Facilities: Scottish National Golf Centre has Gym facilities.
Other Sporting Facilities: Rhynd Country Sports – Clay Shooting, Equestrian Centre, Fishing + Quad Biking.

TARIFF

Normal Tarriff
Sharing twin/double*
B&B £57.50 (Executive Rooms add £17.50pppn)
D,B&B £57.50 (Executive Rooms add £17.50pppn)
*Single Supplement £20.00pppn.

High Season Golf Packages
Sharing twin/double*
2 nights, D,B&B inc Golf £135.00
(Executive Rooms add £17.50pppn).
3 nights D,B&B inc Golf £192.00
(Executive Rooms add £17.50pppn).
*Single Supplement £20.00pppn
Please Call for Winter Rates, Christmas and New Year Packages.

DIRECTIONS

Drumoig is situated on the main Dundee to St Andrews road (A92/A914) four miles from Dundee and eight miles from St Andrews.

The Gleneagles Hotel

Golf at Gleneagles is a blend of natural experience and golfing adventure on three championship courses set in the splendour of the Perthshire hills. The courses were the inspiration of two of the world's most famous golfers, James Braid, five times winner of the Open championship who designed the King's and Queen's, and Jack Nicklaus, Golfer of the Century, who designed the Monarch's. The King's and Queen's, opened in 1919, represent the finest 'classical' golf course design. The King's is a masterpiece of design which has tested the aristocracy of golf, both professional and amateur.

The natural beauty of the Queen's inspires the world's most experienced players. The Monarch's opened in 1993, is a 'modern classic', combining the best of both earlier designs. The fun Par 3 Wee Course is a light alternative for both beginners and experts and recalls the original nine-hole course at Gleneagles, constructed in 1928 by the head greenkeeper, George Alexander, and staff from the hotel.

Gleneagles provides five star services for both guests and golfers. Caddies; pull carts; petrol-driven carts on the Monarch's; professional instructors who teach and play with guests; club and shoe hire.

Gleneagles means golf - but it also means so much more. Our guests often debate whether staying at Gleneagles is more relaxing than vigorous or the other way round. There are walks, riding, shooting, fishing, tennis, croquet and mountain biking - all with expert help and tuition. For more gentler indoor pursuits try billiards, a quiet swim in our pool or shopping for gifts in the arcade of top class shops within the hotel.

From your first wholehearted Scottish welcome you will be looked after warmly and well. Take time to enjoy the splendid interiors of our hotel where kings and queens, the stars and the successful have admired the grandeur and elegance of this famous resort.

Choose from 222 luxurious bedrooms, including 14 exclusively decorated suites. Several luxurious new bedrooms are now available. Designed in classic contemporary style these are part of a £5 million major refurbishment programme at the Five Red Star hotel.

The bedrooms, in muted colours with sensual fabrics and with spacious bathrooms, will ensure that guests enjoy the finest comforts and the ultimate in relaxation.

At Gleneagles you'll find a world of ease and comfort, time to unwind and reflect.

LOCAL ATTRACTIONS

Gleneagles is surrounded by great castles and stately homes such as Blair Castle, ancestral seat of the Duke of Atholl, chief of the Clan Murray and the only British subject allowed to maintain a private army, the Atholl Highlanders; and Scone Palace, site of the ancient crowning place of Scottish kings and now home to the Earls of Mansfield

GOLF INFORMATION

18 hole, 6471 yard (King's course)
18 hole, 5969 yard (Queen's course)
18 hole, 6134 yard (Monarch's course)
All Parkland
Par 70/68/72

Golf Professional: Greg Schofield Tel: +44 (0)1764 694343

Practice Facilities: Covered driving range, video teaching, short and long game area, putting green.

Instructions: Groups and individuals catered for.

Hire: Clubs and buggies

Green Fees: Per person per round.
April and October 2000 £85.00
May to September 2000 £100.00
November 2000 to March 2001 £75.00

CARD OF THE COURSE					
Kings course					
1	362	Par 4	10	447	Par 4
2	405	Par 4	11	230	Par 3
3	374	Par 4	12	395	Par 4
4	466	Par 4	13	448	Par 4
5	161	Par 3	14	260	Par 4
6	476	Par 5	15	459	Par 4
7	439	Par 4	16	135	Par 3
8	158	Par 3	17	377	Par 4
9	354	Par 4	18	525	Par 5
Out	3327	Par 35	In	3276	Par 35

PERTHSHIRE

HOTEL INFORMATION

The Gleneagles Hotel,
Auchterarder, Perthshire, Scotland.
PH3 1NF
Tel: +44 (0) 1764 662231
Fax: +44 (0) 1764 662134
Rating: AA 5 Red Star
Rooms: 229, 14 of which are exclusively decorated suites.
Restaurants: Gleneagles has three resaurants, Strathearn - three rosette award winning restaurant, The Club restaurant and The Dormy Clubhouse.
Childcare facilities: Playroom and child activity area.
Sporting Facilities: Equestrian, Shooting, Falconry, fresh and sea fishing, tennis, lawn bowls, croquet, jogging.
Other Leisure Activities: Off road driving.

TARIFF

B&B + 18 holes:
From £215.00 per person
per night.

**Other special
golf packages:**
One day package (Sat-Sun)
May - Sept Twighlight golf after
5pm - £55.00 (golf only).

Weekend breaks:
Rooms only from £160.00 per
person, Golf packages from £232
per person.

DIRECTIONS

The Quickest route is usually via the M1 - M6 motorways. After Carlisle, follow signs for Glasgow, taking the A74 - M74. Leave the M74 at junction 4 and take the M73 signed to Stirling. This will lead you onto the A80, then the M80.
Take the M80 North and join the M9 signed to Perth. When the M9 becomes the A9, follow the local directions as detailed above. *Do not be tempted to take the direction signed to "Gleneagles" as this goes to a private estate and is in the opposite direction to the hotel

Letham Grange Resort

*L*etham Grange Resort is situated amidst serene countryside at the heart of Carnoustie country, which is an area of 842 square miles on the east coast of Scotland, between Dundee and Aberdeen. with 60 courses within 60 minutes.

A wonderfully restored baronial mansion, Letham Grange offers a warm welcome to all who visit. Reflecting the Victorian era, many of the original features of the house remain. These are sympathetically enhanced by many, modern comforts on and around the estate.

The centrepiece of Letham Grange is undoubtedly the old course. Officially opened for play in April 1987, the course makes splendid and often dramatic use of the grandeur of the estate. The course incorporates water hazards, narrow fairways and undulating terrain. Water is a permanent feature of the course and can be found on 13 of the 18 holes. The par 3, 8th is played over a picturesque lake onto a green surrounded by mature trees and rhododendrons. No wonder this is Known as the 'Augusta of Scotland'.

The Par 68 Glens Course is now 8 years old and is equally testing if shorter than the old course and is great value.

GOLF INFORMATION

18hole, 6968 yard (Old Course)
18 hole, 5528 yard (Glens Course)
Both parkland course
Par 73/68

Golf Professional: Steven Moir
Tel: 01241 890 373

Instructions: Groups and individuals catered for by arrangement with out Golf Professional.

Hire: Clubs and buggies.

Green Fees:	Old	Glens
Weekday	£35.00	£20.00.
Weekend	£45.00	£25.00

CARD OF THE COURSE

Old Course			Glens Course		
1	363	Par 4	1	380	Par 4
2	357	Par 4	2	273	Par 4
3	500	Par 5	3	367	Par 4
4	403	Par 4	4	172	Par 3
5	161	Par 3	5	484	Par 5
6	519	Par 5	6	160	Par 3
7	402	Par 4	7	352	Par 4
8	176	Par 3	8	193	Par 3
9	553	Par 5	9	396	Par 4
Out	3434	Par 37	Out	2794	Par 34
10	391	Par 4	10	411	Par 4
11	440	Par 4	11	485	Par 5
12	204	Par 3	12	173	Par 3
13	359	Par 4	13	369	Par 4
14	541	Par 5	14	354	Par 4
15	218	Par 3	15	294	Par 4
16	426	Par 4	16	153	Par 3
17	527	Par 5	17	359	Par 4
18	428	Par 4	18	136	Par 3
In	3534	Par 36	Out	2734	Par 34

ANGUS

HOTEL INFORMATION

Letham Grange Resort
Colliston by Arbroath,
Angus DD11 4RL
Tel: 01241 890 373
Fax: 44 (0)1241 890 725
Rating: AA 4 Star, RAC 4 Star, Scottish Tourist Board 4 Star.
Rooms: 42.
Restaurants: Rosehaugh formal restaurant + Golfer's retreat restaurant and conservatory.
Fitness Facilities: Nearby fitness facilities at the Saltire centre.
Other Sporting Facilites: Lawn tennis, croquet, fishing and numerous outdoor sports nearby.
Other Leisure Activities: See our website: www.lethamgrange.co.uk

TARIFF

B&B Summer (April-Sept 2000)
Single (in Dbl.-Std. Room) £100
Twin/Double Standard £155
Executive Suites £210
Rapunzel Suite £310
B&B Winter (Oct 98 – Mar 99)
Single (in Dbl.-Std. Room) £80
Twin/Double Standard £110
Executive Suites £170
Rapunzel Suite £260

Hotel residents recieve a 30% golf discount.

Special Golf Packages:
Eagle Golf Breaks from £89.00 per person including accommodation + dinner + round of golf.
Special off season rates in Spring and Autumn.
Society golfers welcome.

DIRECTIONS

Travelling by road from Glagow.
Take the A80/M80 to Stirling, then follow the A9/M9 to Perth and take the A90 to Dundee. Take the A92 to Arbroath and then the A933 towards Brechin. Take the 1st right after Colliston for Letham Grange. (Follow the tourist board signs from anywhere within 5 miles).

Marriott Dalmahoy Hotel & Country Club

*T*he main house at Dalmahoy, a Georgian style mansion sheltering under the rolling Pentland Hills, looks out across a thousand acres of woodland estates towards Edinburgh Castle.

There are 215 bedrooms, many having fine views of the golf courses and the estate

LOCAL ATTRACTIONS

One of the main reasons for staying at Marriott Dalmahoy must lie in its convenience to Edinburgh with its numerous galleries and museums. Take in the shopping of Princes Street and the history of Holyrood Palace and the Royal Mile. Move slightly further afield and see some of the ancient crafts on display in the tartan mills and malt distilleries.

grounds. The House's seven original bedrooms have been carefully restored and give a clear idea of how Dalmahoy was furnished in the 18th century.

The Pentland Restaurant, overlooking the lake with a sweeping view beyond to Edinburgh, offers a particularly friendly atmosphere for relaxed dining. A more informal setting is provided by the Long Weekend Café Bar beside the heated swimming pool.

The two courses at Dalmahoy offer enjoyable and taxing rounds where you play against a backdrop of wooded countryside with lakes and streams. The West Course has two quite spectacular crossings of the Gogar Burn, while the famous East Course will provide you with golf to a truly international standard – this course hosted the Solheim Cup in 1992 and regularly hosts the Scottish PGA Championship. Designed by James Braid in 1923 it has some exceedingly tricky holes, such as the par 3 15th, known as 'The Wee Wrecker'.

GOLF INFORMATION

West Course, 5185 yards, par 68, 18-hole. East Course, 6677 yards, par 72, 18-hole.

Practice facilities: Large putting greens, two short game practice greens, 12 bay all-weather floodlit driving range.

Instructions: Tuition available.

Hire: Trolley, buggy, club and shoe hire.

CARD OF THE COURSE
West Course

1	278	Par 4	10	170	Par 3
2	279	Par 4	11	365	Par 4
3	128	Par 3	12	344	Par 4
4	373	Par 4	13	540	Par 5
5	310	Par 4	14	311	Par 4
6	271	Par 4	15	339	Par 4
7	262	Par 4	16	117	Par 3
8	437	Par 4	17	172	Par 3
9	180	Par 3	18	309	Par 4
Out	2518	Par 34	In	2667	Par 34

HOTEL INFORMATION

Marriott Dalmahoy Hotel & Country Club
Kirknewton, Nr Edinburgh
Scotland EH27 8EB
Tel: 0131 333 1845
Fax: 0131 333 1433
Rooms: 215.
Restaurants: Pentland Restaurant, Long Weekend Café Bar, Cocktail Bar and Club Bar.
Health and Beauty: Health and Beauty salon, Solarium.
Other Fitness Facilities: Indoor heated swimming pool, spa bath, sauna, steam room, fully equipped gymnasium, dance studio.
Other Sporting Facilities: Riding, fishing, clay pigeon shooting, Tennis courts, Trim/jogging trail.

TARIFF

DINNER, BED & BREAKFAST
(Mon-Sun)

Prices start from **£79** per person, per night (low season), including a round of golf on the East Course. Based on two sharing.

DIRECTIONS

Dalmahoy can be found approximately 7 miles west of Edinburgh on the A71. Edinburgh Airport is 3 miles away.
The hotel is 45 minutes drive from Glasgow and just 5 minutes from the M8.

THE ROXBURGHE HOTEL & GOLF COURSE

Kelso, Roxburghshire, TD5 8JZ. Tel: 01573 450331 Fax: 01573 450611
Web: www.roxburghe.net E-mail: hotel@roxburghe.net

18 HOLES	PAR 72
7111 YARDS	
TYPE OF GOLF COURSE: Parkland	
RATING: STB 4 Star	
GOLF PROFESSIONAL: Gordon Niven TEL: 01573 450333	
B&B + 18 HOLES: Rooms from £120.00. Golf £40.00.	

This luxury country house hotel owned by the Duke and Duchess of Roxburghe is situated in quiet parkland and features elegant reception rooms, 22 individually designed bedrooms including four posters and suites. The AA2 Rossette restaurant offers excellent service and superb cuisine.

The 18 hole championship standard course, designed by Dave Thomas has deep challenging bunkers, dramatic water hazards and generous rolling greens. A health and beauty clinic, clay pigeon shooting, fishing, tennis and croquet, practice ground and putting green are all on site.

MURRAYSHALL HOUSE HOTEL & GOLF COURSE

Scone, Perth PH2 7PH. Tel: 01738 551171
Fax: 01738 552595

HOLES: 18	YARDS: 6441	PAR: 73

OLD COURSE HOTEL GOLF RESORT & SPA

St. Andrews, Kingdom of Fife KY16 9SP.
Tel: 01334 474371   Fax: 01334 477668

HOLES: 18	YARDS: 7271	PAR: 72

Castle Fraser, Grampian Highlands

Northern Ireland

Antrim,
Carrick-A-Rede Rope Bridge

Northern Ireland

*T*he continued efforts to find a lasting solution to the "Troubles" in Northern Ireland is good and bad news for golfers. Good news for those who have not sampled the glorious links of this province, but bad news for those who have been coming here for years, despite the threat imposed by militants on either side of the divide.

In all honesty the "Troubles" haven't really affected the pace of play that much. The golf course has been the one place to escape the sectarian extra-curricular activities. And what safe havens they are.

You'll struggle to find better links golf than that to be found in the province of Ulster. Just an hour's drive north of Belfast you'll find links courses to satisfy any dyed in the wool traditionalist. Royal Portrush, Portstewart, Castlerock, Ballycastle, they offer all the fun of seaside golf.

Of course Portrush is the jewel of this coastline. Still the only course outside mainland Britain to have staged the Open Championship – when Max Faulkner captured the Old Claret Jug in 1951 – Portrush is a true championship course in an age when that particular adjective has been devalued by modern golf course builders. Huge sand dunes, tight fairways, pot bunkers, undulating greens – in short everything you expect of seaside golf. It's a course that has been used for many important championships, amateur and professional alike. Look for it to return to the Open rota one day when the political scenario is much more favourable.

Anyone travelling to this coastline, to the Giant's Causeway – dubbed as such because of the strange geological rock formation where land meets sea, rocks which look like steps down into the cold waters of the Irish sea – needs to make a proper job of the visit. To do that you must play Portstewart, Castlerock and Ballycastle. Along with Portrush, these three courses provide the venue for the Blackbush, a huge amateur event held every June that attracts hundreds of golfers. All three are special in their own way. For example, Portstewart offers some of the best natural golf to be found anywhere. The new holes constructed in the dunes in the late 80s would not look out of place on Portrush, or any other great links course for that matter. Play them to your handicap and you'll be one happy golfer. Indeed, play this course to your handicap and you have either had a great day or you should be wearing a mask.

Castlerock and Ballycastle don't quite come up to the standard of Portrush and Portstewart, but they are very enjoyable. Castlerock is a wonderfully natural links with a good mix of testing and enjoyable holes. Ballycastle may be short but don't let that put you off. Play it first of the quartet – it's the perfect course to hone your game for the challenges of the other three.

If it's challenge your after, then you'll find it about two and a half hours south of Portrush, at Newcastle, home to Royal County Down.

Another magnificent links course, this one is even more natural than the ones to be found on the Causeway Coast. Here you'll find plenty of blind shots, especially from the tee, where you aim at a marker stone or post and fire away. It's long too, so don't play it off the back markers unless you've got your A game with you. If you haven't then fear not, the Mountains of Mourne provide a splendid backdrop for those content to look at the scenery.

Don't think golf in the province of Ulster is all played by the sea. It isn't. There's plenty of parkland challenges to satisfy those who don't like the wind to mess their hair. Malone, Belvoir Park, Clandeboye's two fine courses – the Ava and the Dufferin – are just a few of the courses for those who want a break from the sea.

Northern Ireland

Page

Silverwood Golf Hotel & Country Club

*T*he Silverwood Golf Hotel and Country Club, situated in pleasant rural surroundings is only 2 minutes from the M1 motorway which links the hotel to Belfast and within 20 minutes of the air/seaports.

Over the years the hotel has built up a reputation for excellent food combined with friendly and efficient service in a relaxed and charming setting together with a 24-hour check-in service. Each of the 29 large bedrooms is luxuriously furnished with a bathroom en-suite and telephone, radio, CD and tape deck, satellite television, trouser press, iron and ironing board, hairdryer and tea/coffee making facilities. A number of executive rooms are also available. The dining room, in light sunny colours with pine and wicker furniture is extremely popular with both residents and locals. The lounge provides a carvery lunch and an extensive snack menu daily. The Topaz night club features live bands at the weekend as well as music in the lounge bar.

The Silverwood Golf/Ski Centre on site consists of an 18 hole parkland course, a 9 hole par 3 course, a pitch and putt course, putting greens and a floodlit driving range. The course has sand based well irrigated greens and has lakes incorporated into the 3rd and 10th holes.

LOCAL ATTRACTIONS

Northern Ireland's premier ski slope is situated to the front of the hotel. Jet skiing, water skiing, canoeing and windsurfing are available nearby.

In addition sailing, angling and bird watching all take place locally. Two National Trust properties, Ardress House and The Argory are much visited by tourists and have many fine woodland and garden walks.

GOLF INFORMATION

18 hole, 6188 yard parkland course

Par 72

Golf Professional: Des Paul

Tel: 02838 326606

Practice facilities: Covered driving range.

Instructions: Groups and individuals catered for.

Hire: Clubs and trollies.

CARD OF THE COURSE Yellow Tees					
1	396	Par 4	10	487	Par 5
2	539	Par 5	11	157	Par 3
3	314	Par 4	12	335	Par 4
4	310	Par 4	13	303	Par 4
5	141	Par 3	14	430	Par 4
6	417	Par 4	15	203	Par 3
7	422	Par 4	16	303	Par 4
8	376	Par 4	17	311	Par 4
9	455	Par 5	18	289	Par 4
Out	3370	Par 37	In	2818	Par 35

HOTEL INFORMATION

Silverwood Golf Hotel and Country Club
40 Kiln Road, Lurgan, Craigavon
Co. Armagh BT66 6NF.
Tel: 02838 327722
Fax: 02838 325290
Rating: Best Western 3 Star.
Rooms: 29.
Restaurants: Restaurant – English food, wide and varied menu. Lounge Bar – Carvery and extensive bar snack menu.
Childcare Facilities: Baby sitting facilities available.
Hair and Beauty: Available locally
Other Sporting Facilities: Dry ski slope on site, watersports centre – waterskiing, jetsking, canoeing, windsurfing (2 miles from hotel), sailing and boat trips on Lough Neagh. Angling – Lough Neagh and river Bann – both coarse and game fishing, bird watching – Oxford island on Lough Neagh – National Nature Reserve.
Other Leisure Activities: Music in bar at weekends and traditional music midweek, night club attached to hotel with live bands and disco. (Free to Residents). Lurgan public park 200 acres of woodland, lake and recretation areas, Lough Neagh Discovery Centre, Oxford Island – National Nature Reserve with 270 acres and 8km of walks, Discovery Centre tells the story of the history, culture and wildlife around Lough Neagh.

TARIFF

Std. rm: **£55** sgl; **£70** dbl;
Ex. rm: **£65** sgl; **£90** dbl, inc breafast.
Weekend Break:
(Fri/Sat or Sat/Sun) 1 day **£35**pps,
2 days **£65**pps; 3 days **£90**pps –
all weekend rates include B&B + dinners.

Golf Package: (Thurs to Sunday inclusive) 1 day b&b, 1 dinner + 1 day golf **£40;** 2 days b&b, 2 dinners, 2 days golf **£75** pps; 3 days b&b, 3 dinners, 3 days golf **£110**pps. Other packages available on request.

Special Golf Packages:
B&B including 18 holes **£27.50**pps.

DIRECTIONS

From Belfast Seaport & Belfast City Airport - Take the motorway M1 West towards Craigavon and exit at junction 10 on the Craigavon (Lurgan) exit road A76. Continue for about half a mile and take the first right hand turn marked Silverwood Golf/Ski Centre (Kiln Road) continue for about ¼ mile and the hotel lies on the right hand side.

From Belfast International Airport – Take the A26 South to the motorway M1 and enter on the motorway at junction 9. Head west and exit at next junction 10 as above

From Larne Seaport – Take the A8 South to Belfast and follow road to the motorway M1 exit from the M1 at junction 10 and continue as above.

Royal County Down

HILTON TEMPLEPATRICK (will operate as Stakis Park to Spring 2000)
Castle Upton Estate, Templepatrick, County Antrim. Northern Ireland BT39 0DD
Tel: 028 9443 5500 Fax: 028 9443 5511

Set in 220 acres of wooded parkland within the Castle Upton Estate in Templepatrick, County Antrim, Hilton Templepatrick is Northern Ireland's newest four star hotel, conference, golf and leisure resort. With a LivingWell Health Club on site, featuring an 18m swimming pool, sauna, steam room, spa area, gym and all weather tennis courts, you are really spoilt for choice. Set in Sir Robin Kinahan's country estate, the golf course is over 7000 yards and offers challenges to golfers of all abilities. Strategically placed bunkers and spectacular water features, including Co Antrim's Six Mile Water, ensure that the golfer experiences all the excitement that a golf course should offer. There is a full range of practice facilities as well as Kinahan's Bar Bistro which overlooks the 18th green.

18 HOLES	PAR 71	6589 YARDS

TYPE OF GOLF COURSE: Parkland

HOTEL RATING: 4 Star

B&B + 18 HOLES: On application

OTHER SPECIAL GOLF PACKAGES:
On application

RADISSON ROE PARK HOTEL AND GOLF RESORT
Roe Park, Limavady, County Londonderry, BT49 9LB.
Tel: 015047 222222 Fax: 015047 22313

HOLES: 18	YARDS: 6318	PAR: 70

Ardglass

Western Ireland

Dungaire Castle, Kinvara

Western Ireland

*T*here's something haunting about the west coast of Ireland. Maybe it's the wind, perhaps it's the emptiness of the place. Whatever it is it's often an eerie place to be. Just driving through this wild, rugged landscape gives one a feeling of helplessness against the elements. Of course this feeling is truly experienced by walking the coastline, and what better way to do that than with a golf bag on your shoulders?

So many of the courses of the West Coast seem to battle for existence with the Atlantic Ocean. This is where links golf truly lives up to its definition, for one thing you can always count on in the west of Ireland is the wind. Get a calm day on this coastline and you had better take advantage of it, for there aren't many days when the wind doesn't blow.

True there are inland courses to be found here, but you will always be drawn to the coast. From the hidden gems of Donegal – Murvagh, Ballyliffin, Rosapenna, Narin & Portnoo, Northwest – to the great links courses of County Kerry in the South – Ballybunion, Caenn Sibeal, Dooks, Tralee, Waterville – this is links golf par excellence. In between you'll find such classics links as County Sligo, Enniscrone, Lahinch and Connemara.

This is golf as it was meant to be played. Along the ground as opposed to through the air. Bump and run shots, putters from 10 yards off the green, punched iron shots and low flying drivers, you'll need a full repertoire of seaside stroke savers to help you match your handicap.

Some courses, like Ballybunion, Waterville, Tralee, Lahinch are magnets for golfers seeking links golf at its best. In summer you will find plenty of foreigners vying for tee times – Americans, Japanese, Swedes, Germans, golfers of just about every nationality visit these courses through the warmer months. However, there are plenty that have yet to be truly discovered by golfers around the world. The courses of Donegal are still relatively "undiscovered" by foreigners, although their attractions are starting to be broadcast far and wide, particularly the two excellent courses at Ballyliffin. The same goes for the likes of Caenn Sibeal, Enniscrone and the wild landscape of Connemara.

So perseverance is required in the summer months, but if you're willing to take a chance with the elements, then the spring and autumn are often the best times to visit this area.

If it's inland golf your after then fear not. There's plenty of good parkland golf to be found on the west coast of the Emerald Isle. Adare Manor, Beaufort, Galway Bay, and of course Killarney Golf and Fishing Club, venue for the Irish Open on a number of occasions. The two courses here are as pretty and as challenging as you are ever likely to find. Of course the beauty of the place is enhanced by the magnificent Macgillicuddy Reeks, Ireland's tallest mountain range, which tower over the two excellent parkland layouts.

However, the inland venues are just a pleasant distraction. If you want to play traditional Irish golf at its best, then head for the sea.

Western Ireland

Page

Adare Manor Hotel & Country Club

S et in the South West of Ireland, Adare Manor is a 5 star luxury resort nestling in 840 acres of rolling countryside complete with it's own championship golf course. As rich in beauty as it is in history, the Manor is an architectural jewel presiding over breathtaking formal gardens, majestic parkland and fascinating ruins dating back over eight hundred years. This 5 star Manor House Hotel has 63 deluxe rooms in the Manor House. At the Golf Village there are 11 Carriage House Suites, 18 two bedroom and seven four bedroom Golf Cottages and 18,000 sq foot Clubhouse comprising bar, restaurant, conference centre, pro shop, ladies and gents locker rooms.

The magnificent public rooms include the Long Gallery, a warm and cosy library and the exquisitely appointed Cocktail Lounge. The hotels' restaurant overlooks the River Maigue and specialises in the best of modern Irish cuisine with all of the ingredients being sourced in the region.

The par 72, Robert Trent Jones senior designed course is rated as one of the finest this great man has completed and Adare has joined the list of top courses designed by him which include Spy Glass Hills and Peachtree in the US, Las Brisas and Valderrama in Spain.

The course is gentle parkland making it a pleasure to walk but testing with water at 10 holes including the last which is particularly challenging.

LOCAL ATTRACTIONS

Within the estate there is fishing on the River Maigue, horse riding and clay pigeon shooting. The village of Adare is right at the front gate and some of the great golf courses in Ireland's Southwest, Ballybunion, Killarney, Lahinch and Tralee are an hour's drive away.

GOLF INFORMATION

18 hole, 7138 yard Heathland/Woodland course Par 72

Tel: 61 395 044

Practice facilities: Outdoor driving range.

Instructions: Groups and individuals catered for.

Hire: Clubs and buggies.

LIMERICK

CARD OF THE COURSE					
1	433	Par 4	10	441	Par 4
2	413	Par 4	11	187	Par 3
3	403	Par 4	12	550	Par 5
4	180	Par 3	13	442	Par 4
5	419	Par 4	14	425	Par 4
6	205	Par 3	15	370	Par 4
7	537	Par 5	16	170	Par 3
8	427	Par 4	17	415	Par 4
9	577	Par 5	18	544	Par 5
Out	3594	Par 36	In	3544	Par 36

HOTEL INFORMATION

Adare Manor Hotel & Golf Club
Adare, Co Limerick Ireland
Tel: 61 396566
Fax: 61 396124
Rating: 5 Star RAC, Small Luxury Hotels
Rooms: 63.
Restaurants: Formal dining in Restaurant – Formal dining in Oak Room Restaurant, Casual dining in Clubhouse Restaurant.
Childcare Facilities: 24hr childcare service available on request.
Hair and Beauty: Available on request
Fitness Facilities: Indoor swimming pool, Fitness centre, Massage Therapy.
Other Sporting Facilities: Golf on our Championship courses, Clay Pigeon Shooting, Fishing (Gillies available), Hunting and Horse Riding.

TARIFF

From **£145** room only – January to March, November to December 2000
£185 room only – April to October
£240 room only – May to September.

Special Golf Packages:
3 and 5 day Packages available on request.

DIRECTIONS

Only 24 miles from Shannon Airport, Adare Manor is 9 miles from Limerick city. From Limerick City, follow the N20 through the village of Patrickswell; then take the N21 to the village of Adare. The entrance to the estate of Adare Manor is right at the start of the village street.

209

Glenlo Abbey Hotel

*W*e invite you to Glenlo Abbey Hotel, you will enjoy an unrivalled personal service, in the warmth of one of Ireland's exclusive five star luxury hotels.

This 5 Star Hotel stands in an 138 acre estate overlooking Lough Corrib situated just 2.5 miles (4km) from Galway City.

LOCAL ATTRACTIONS

Aran Island can be visited by boat the trip takes about 90 minutes from Galway Bay or by plane, which will give you a superb aerial view over Dun Aengus.

On the Island you will find an impressive Bronze Age Fort of Dun Aengus (over 2000 years old) plus many other ancient monuments.

Partake of award winning Irish and International cuisine. In the Pullman Restaurant aboard the Orient Express you can savour the charm and elegance of this world famous luxury train for an unforgettable dining experience. Our River Room is an ideal choice for dinner, receptions and banquets. For 'chat and craic' and more informal dining check out the Oak Cellar Bar.

We take the work out of your business. Our self contained fully serviced conference facilities are suitable for any type of corporate or social occasion. Accommodating from 4 to 250 people our corporate facilities offer cutting edge support to your company. With several meeting and conference rooms and a fully equipped business service bureau we make your business with us work for you.

A host of outdoor activities on your doorstep include a challenging nine hole golf course with double greens. Our Driving Range and Putting Greens ensure that you are well practiced by the time you get on the course. Enjoy the ultimate in Lough Corrib. Clay Pigeon Shooting and many other activities are available on - site or nearby.

GOLF INFORMATION

9 holes with two greens, 6538 yard Parkland with a view Par 71

Golf Professional: Philip Murphy
Tel: 091 579698 Fax: 091 579699

Practice Facilities: Covered Driving range, Golf tec computer, out door grass tees.

Instructions: Groups and individuals catered for.

Hire: Clubs and buggies.

CARD OF THE COURSE

1	389	Par 4	10	413	Par 4
2	430	Par 4	11	430	Par 4
3	399	Par 4	12	361	Par 4
4	163	Par 3	13	179	Par 3
5	370	Par 4	14	366	Par 4
6	416	Par 4	15	470	Par 5
7	204	Par 3	16	177	Par 3
8	492	Par 5	17	492	Par 5
9	383	Par 4	18	404	Par 4
Out	3246	Par 35	In	3292	Par 36

HOTEL INFORMATION

Glenlo Abbey Hotel, Bushypark, Galway. Ireland
Tel: +353 91 526666
Fax: +353 91 527800
email: glenlo@iol.ie
www: www.glenlo.com
Rating: AA Red Star, RAC Blue Ribbons, AA Rosettes for cuisine, AA Romantic Hotel of GB&IR.
Rooms: 45 Spacious Bedrooms including Suites.
Restaurants: Pullman Restaurant aboard the Orient Express, River Room Restaurant, Oak Cellar Bar.
Other Sporting Facilities: Clay pigeon shooting, lake fishing or boating, tennis, riding.
Other Leisure Activities: Sailing and windsurfing

TARIFF

B&B + 18 holes:
On Request

Weekend Breaks:
On Request.

Other Special Golf Packages:
Stay 8 play with tuition.

DIRECTIONS

Dublin ½ hour
Frankfurt 2½ hours
Paris 1¾ hours
Brussels 1¾ hours
London 1¼ hours
New York 8 to 10 hours

Rosapenna Golf Hotel

*T*he quality of the golf, unlimited access to the Links, and the superb facilities in the hotel, have attracted golfers to Rosapenna for generations.

Here you can golf in a golfing atmosphere, enjoy the genuinely warm Donegal hospitality and drink in the wonderful scenery and pure Atlantic air. The food is fresh from the unpolluted sea, rivers, lakes and land. The bar is friendly and spacious while the bedrooms

LOCAL ATTRACTIONS

Mount Errigal, the highest mountain in Donegal is close by, as is Glenveagh National Park, Ards Forest Park and historic Doe Castle. You can enjoy traditional music in a number of friendly Donegal pubs, hire a bike or ramble and savour the unspoilt scenery at a leisurely pace.

offer a relaxing ambience where you can recharge the batteries for the next day's golf.

In 1895 the club was instituted, Tom Morris's design was later modified by two other great masters of the game, James Braid and Harry Vardon. Rosapenna is, to this day, one of the great natural golf courses in Ireland. Only three of the 18 greens had to be laid as the other 15 are a vindication of Tom Morris's judgement of the turf.

A combination of natural links and inland holes, the first ten holes play along Sheephaven Bay between the beach and a range of tall sand dunes. The last eight play inland and uphill in meadow where the high grounds present distracting and delightful views.

Rosapenna organises golf clinics and golf learning programmes for all classes of golfer. The clinics are run for groups which are kept deliberately small in order to focus attention on the individual.

Should you wish to mix golf with a touring holiday, you could not be better placed. The peninsulas round Mulroy and Sheephaven bays will take your breath away for sheer beauty and majesty.

GOLF INFORMATION

**18-holes 6271 yards, par 70.
Parkland**

Golf Professional: Tel 074-55128

Green Fees: Weekdays - IR£22 per round
Weekend + Irish B/H IR£27 per round
Weekdays (day) - IR£30. Weekends (day) - IR£35.

Holes: 27

CARD OF THE COURSE					
1	298	Par 4	10	543	Par 5
2	428	Par 4	11	427	Par 4
3	446	Par 4	12	342	Par 4
4	386	Par 4	13	455	Par 4
5	255	Par 4	14	128	Par 3
6	167	Par 3	15	418	Par 4
7	367	Par 4	16	216	Par 3
8	485	Par 5	17	358	Par 4
9	185	Par 3	18	367	Par 4
Out 3017 Par 35			In 3254 Par 35		

HOTEL INFORMATION

Rosapenna Hotel & Golf Links
Downings, County Donegal,
Ireland
Tel: 00353 7455301
Fax: 00353 7455128
Rooms: 53
Rating: 4
Restaurants: 1 main dining room serving a 5
course meal from 7.30 to 8.45.
Other Fitness Facilities: Swimming pool, steam
room and Spa, which will hopefully open early
spring 2000.

TARIFF

D,B&B + Green Fees
July/Aug 2days IR£152.00
May/June 2days IR£142.00
Mar/Apr 2days IR£132.00
(Per person Sharing)

B&B Packages
July/Aug Single IR£67.00
Twin IR£110.00
May/June Single IR£64.50
Twin IR£105.00
Mar/Apr Single IR£62.00
Twin IR£100.00

Concessionary Green Fees on B/B
IR£15.00 per day.

DIRECTIONS

Approx 112 miles from
Belfast International
airport, via Londonderry,
Letter Kenny, Milford,
Carrigaret. We are
situated 1½ miles from
Carrigart on the Rosguill
peninsula. Beside village of
Downings.
By Road, M2 or A6 to Londonderry
N13 from Londonderry to Letter
Kenny, R245 from Letter Kenny to
Downings.

Lakes of Killarney, Co Kerry

CLONLARA GOLF & LEISURE
Clonlara, Co. Clare. Tel: 061 354141 Fax: 0161 354143

12 HOLES	PAR 47	3377 METRES

TYPE OF GOLF COURSE: Parkland

RATING: 2/3 Star

B&B + 18 HOLES:
Self-catering Apartments

Clonlara Golf & Leisure is ideally situated, being in the heart of the West of Ireland and only a 20 minute drive from the centre of Limerick City.
It is located on the grounds of Landscape House, which was built in the 17th Century, and is now the private residence of Mr and Mrs O'Connell. The 12-hole (Par 47) golf course stands on 63 acres of mature parkland.
Whether you are on holiday in the area and would enjoy the pleasure of a leisurely game, or a golf society planning an outing, we will be more than please to welcome you. Accommodation is in self-catering apartments. Tennis, sauna, pool & table tennis are also available and a children's play area.

DROMOLAND CASTLE GOLF & COUNTRY CLUB
Newmarket on Fergus, Co. Clare. Tel: 061-368144 Fax: 061-363355

Built in the late 16th century, Dromoland Castle forms a majestic backdrop to the challenging course that bears its name. 18 holes since 1985 with a par of 71, Dromoland Golf & Country has earned an enviable reputation both for the quality of golf and the amenities of the new clubhouse, which include a fully equipped health & leisure centre and the brasserie style Fig Tree restaurant.

18 HOLES	PAR 71	6098 YARDS
TYPE OF GOLF COURSE: Parkland		
RATING: Relais & Chateau, AA		
GOLF PROFESSIONAL: Philip Murphy		
TEL: 061-351874		
B&B + 18 HOLES: High Season from £220 per room – Breakfast £13.50pp + 15% SC – Golf £19 – Resident.		

GALWAY BAY GOLF & COUNTRY CLUB HOTEL
Oranmore, Co. Galway, Ireland. Tel: +353 91 790500 Fax: +353 91 792510

Luxury golf and accommodation base situated 8 miles from Galway City in an idyllic setting on the west coast of Ireland. Located overlooking Galway Bay and the Atlantic Ocean 18 hole championship golf course designed by Christy O'Connor Jnr.

Meeting room/conference facilities also available. 2 AA rosettes awarded Grainne Uaile Restaurant.

18 HOLES	PAR 72	6533 YARDS
TYPE OF GOLF COURSE: Parkland/Coastal		
GOLF PROFESSIONAL: Eugene O'Connor TEL: +353 91 790503		
B&B + 18 HOLES: Oct '98–Apr '99 Mon-Fri £59 p.p.s Sat-Sun £63 p.p.s Until End Sept '98 Mon-Fri £84 p.p.s Sat-Sun £88 p.p.s.		
OTHER SPECIAL GOLF PACKAGES: Mid-week Breaks from £119 p.p.s. (2 B&B, 1 dinner + 1 golf).		

GREAT SOUTHERN HOTEL, PARKNASILLA
Parknasilla, Sneem, Co. Kerry.
Tel: +353 64 45122 Fax: +353 64 45323

HOLES: 9	YARDS: 5520	PAR: 70

LIMERICK COUNTY GOLF & COUNTRY CLUB
Ballyneety, Co. Limerick
Tel: 061 351881 Fax: 016 351384 Web:
www.limerickcounty.com Email: lcgolf@ioi.ie

HOLES: 18	YARDS: 6434	PAR: 72

Dublin &
Southern Ireland

Powerscourt Gardens, Co. Wicklow

Dublin & Southern Ireland

With flights to Ireland as cheap and as numerous as they've ever been, there's no reason for anyone not to pay a visit to Dublin and the Emerald isle. Of course if you already live there, then that's the least of your worries. With the road system in Ireland improving all the time, Dublin isn't the trek from other parts of Ireland that it once was.

As a golfer you cannot not go to Ireland to play golf. And if you haven't been to Dublin then what are you waiting for? It's the ideal city break if you enjoy this madly frustrating game. For what could be finer than a round on one of the city's truly great links and a night on the town trying to find the best pint of black stuff in the capital?

Portmarnock, Portmarnock Hotel & Golf Links, The European Club, Druid's Glen, Royal Dublin, Woodbrook, the Seapoint, County Louth, The Island, they, and many more, are within easy striking range of the Irish capital.

First and foremost on your list must be the two links courses at Portmarnock. The Old is hard to get access to but persevere, for it is arguably the best course in all of Ireland. The younger brother, the new links course at Portmarnock Hotel, is no weak relation either. Designed by Bernhard Langer, this is a truly great addition to Irish golf.

So are the newer inland courses such as Druid's Glen, The K Club, St Margaret's and Mount Juliet, a couple of hours to the South. Indeed, the last 10 or 15 years has seen a great explosion in Irish golf courses.

However, as usual it will be the classics of Irish golf that you'll want to play – and their are some outstanding ones. Besides the already mentioned Portmarnock Old, you must try County Louth at Baltray, one of the classic hidden gems in Irish golf, a traditional links course you'll want to take home with you. And if you *have the chance then play Seapoint next door. Veteran European Tour pro Des Smyth is responsible for a good course that is a mixture of links and parkland. You may just want to sneak that course into your suitcase as well.*

The same can be said about The European Club south of Dublin at Brittas Bay. Although it was only opened in 1989, play it for the first time and you'll swear it's been there for 100 years at least. It is arguably architect Pat Ruddy's finest creation, and he's been responsible for a fair few in Ireland.

In the south of the country, try the Jack Nicklaus creation of Mount Juliet, North of Waterford, a course favoured by Nick Faldo and one that has hosted the Irish Open. This is a beautiful parkland course that plays long and tough. Be advised: play it off forward markers.

No matter what markers you play off at the Old Head of Kinsale, you'll probably forget about golf and simply enjoy the view. This course is built in perhaps the most scenic location in all of Ireland – and that's saying something, for there a lot of courses with stunning scenery in the Emerald Isle.

However, the Old Head Links is set on a rocky promontory a few miles south of the town of Kinsale. You drive through a narrow isthmus high above the sea onto an outcrop just big enough for 18 holes. No less than nine holes are played along the edge of the cliffs. Often if you hook or slice then the ball ends up in the sea. It is truly spectacular stuff, but then you know that once you get to the clubhouse, for the views on a fine day are worth the green fee. A must for anyone travelling to this part of Ireland.

So too are the courses at West Waterford, Waterford Castle, Faithlegg, Tramore and St Helen's Bay. Good golf is to be found at all, but then it's hard not to find good golf in this part of Ireland.

Dublin & Southern Ireland

Slieve
Russell
N3
Carrickmacross
N53
Dundalk
N1
Ballymascanlon
House
Nuremore
N52
Ardee
Dunleer
N52
N2
Kells
Slane
Drogheda
N51
Navan
Athboy
Balbriggan
N3
N2
N1
Portmarnock
Links
Hotel
N4
M4
M1
Deerpark
Hotel
N41
Maynooth
Clane
Citywest
Country
House
N7
Dublin
Dun
Laoghaire
Naas
M7
M11
Charlesland
N9
N81
Kildare
Powerscourt
N11
Ballymore
Eustace
N78
Rathsallagh
House
Kilkea
Castle
Glendalough
Wicklow
Baltinglass
Rathdrum
Arklow
Kilkenny
N80
N8
Cashel
ary
N9
Mount
Juliet
N10
N76
Enniscorthy
N9
New
Ross
N79
N11
N24
Clonmel
Carrick-
on-Suir
N25
N25
Waterford
Wexford
St Helen's
Bay
Bridgetown
Waterford
Castle
Fethard
Rosslare
Harbour
N25
Tramore
Cappoquin
2
Dungarvan
Youghal
N25

Faithlegg House Hotel

*F*aithlegg House Hotel, which opened in May 1999, is located on the already renowned 18-hole Faithlegg championship golf course, overlooking the estuary of the River Suir.

The 18th century manor house has been tastefully refurbished and extended to incorporate 82 bedrooms, including 14 master bedrooms in the old house and a unique fitness, health and beauty club which offers a full range of facilities supervised by massage therapists and fitness co-ordinators. Guest

LOCAL ATTRACTIONS

Scenic Drives include, Comeragh Mountains and Nire Valley, Lismore and Vee, Gaeltacht region, Suir Valley, Blackwater Valley.

will enjoy preferred green fees and tee times on Faithlegg golf course

The championship course was designed by Patrick Merrigan to take full advantage of the wonderful wooded landscape on the estuary of the River Suir with Faithlegg House providing a dramatic backdrop to the 18th Green. The par 72 course, fully mature, features gently undulating fairways and boldly contoured greens.

The Faithlegg estate has matured over centuries with fine trees and specimen shrubs abounding, especially in the vicinity of the house. New landscaped gardens incorporate many of these specimens and provide a restful area for relaxation or a gentle stroll.

Elegant dining accompanied by fine wines in classic surroundings, the restaurant spans three rooms from a garden conservatory to two ornate drawing rooms in the old house. This will make it particularly adaptable for private dining parties. Food prepared by our chefs will feature local produce especially fresh fish and seafood from Dunmore East and meat from Waterford's pastureland.

The main conference and banqueting hall has a capacity of 200 theatre style or 130 classroom style and has the full range of conference equipment. There are three meeting and syndicate rooms including a dedicated 16 seater boardroom and a former chapel which accommodate up to 50 persons.

GOLF INFORMATION

18 hole 6057 yard, Parkland course Par 72

Golf Professional: Ted Higgins

Tel: 051 382241

Practice facilities: Driving range.

Instruction: Groups and individuals catered for.

Hire: Clubs and buggies hire available.

CARD OF THE COURSE					
1	268	Par 4	10	448	Par 5
2	454	Par 5	11	362	Par 4
3	149	Par 3	12	401	Par 4
4	319	Par 4	13	455	Par 5
5	385	Par 4	14	465	Par 5
6	187	Par 3	15	339	Par 4
7	378	Par 4	16	150	Par 3
8	356	Par 4	17	395	Par 4
9	142	Par 3	18	404	Par 4
Out 3419 Par 38			In 2638 Par 34		

HOTEL INFORMATION

Faithlegg House Hotel, Co. Waterford, Ireland
Tel: 051 382000
Fax: 051 382010
Rooms: 14 Superior and 68 Standard Rooms.

Restaurants: The Restaurant features local produce especially fresh fish, seafood and meat.
Hair and Beauty: Beauty and facial treatments, sunbed and tanning facilities, massage.
Fitness Facilities: Gymnasium, Spa jacuzzi, sauna, steam room.
Other Sporting Facilities:
Walking trails, bicycle rental, horse riding and trekking, fresh water and sea fishing, snooker rooms.

TARIFF

2 Day Package*:
Two nights, twin/double bed including B&B +18 holes.
Prices per person
Feb-Apr £144.00.
May-Sept £160.00.
Oct-Dec £144.00.
*Daily reduction for non golfer.
*Master bedroom supplement £30.00 per room per night.
Bank holiday supplement £15.00.

Other Special Golf Packages:
On Request.

DIRECTIONS

Dublin (100 miles)
Cork (80 miles)
Limerick (80 miles)
Rosslare (45 miles)
Waterford (6 miles)
Airport (4 miles)
Mt. Juliet (20 miles)

Portmarnock Hotel & Golf Links

*P*ortmarnock Hotel and Golf Links is set in splendid surroundings. The house was originally owned by the Jameson family, famous for their Irish Whiskey. Their home has been tastefully converted to an international hotel with the grounds now hosting a magnificent 18 hole Bernhard Langer designed golf links where Darren Clarke is attached as the Touring Professional.

LOCAL ATTRACTIONS

Portmarnock Hotel & Golf Links is located just 11 miles from the bustling shops and traditional pubs of Ireland's capital city, Dublin. Set in a quiet position overlooking the sea between the villages of Portmarnock and Malahide it is the perfect base for so many activities, from golf to clay pigeon shooting, sailing to horse riding. Miles of beautiful beaches provide the enthusiastic walker with ample opportunities to stretch the legs.

The 103 bedrooms are cleverly designed to ensure that you are either looking over the sea or the golf course. A choice of elegantly appointed accommodation is yours, ranging from the historic four-posters, to executive suites and deluxe rooms.

In the Osborne Restaurant, a wonderful choice of international cuisine is served with style and friendliness ... along with a superb selection of wines. In the less formal Links Restaurant, golfers and locals alike can enjoy excellent dining in a relaxed setting.

Like most good new links courses, the new course at Portmarnock looks as if it's been there for a 100 years. Langer has ensured that the course looks as natural as it should given the land it sits on. Great care has been taken to make the course look and feel as traditional as possible. There are no long walks between green and tee and the bunkering is equal to that of the very best seaside layout. Each of the 100 or so bunkers have been carefully revetted, so that you feel as though you're at Muirfield or Carnoustie.

A selection of other interesting pastimes can be arranged for you to enjoy or maybe attempt for the first time. Try your hand at archery, clay pigeon shooting or even quad bikes over our specially designed obstacle course.

GOLF INFORMATION

18 hole, 6260 metres links course

Par 71

Practice facilities: Outdoor practice ground.

Instructions: Groups and individuals catered for.

Hire: Clubs

CARD OF THE COURSE					
1	354	Par 4	10	484	Par 5
2	360	Par 4	11	419	Par 4
3	178	Par 3	12	329	Par 4
4	527	Par 5	13	137	Par 3
5	431	Par 4	14	317	Par 4
6	486	Par 5	15	364	Par 4
7	412	Par 4	16	371	Par 4
8	342	Par 4	17	185	Par 3
9	156	Par 3	18	408	Par 4
Out	3246	Par 36	In	3014	Par 35

DUBLIN

HOTEL INFORMATION

Portmarnock Hotel & Golf Links
Portmarnock
Co. Dublin
Tel: 01 8460611
Fax: 01 8462442

Rating: 4 Star AA & RAC.

Rooms: 103.

Restaurants: Osbourne – International, Links – Brasserie.

Childcare Facilities: Babysitting available.

Hair and Beauty: on request

Other Sporting Facilities: 18 hole links golf course – designed by B. Langer.

TARIFF

Standard Daily Rates:
Standard: IR£140 Sgl.
IR£205 Twin/Dbl
Executive: IR£170 Sgl.
IR£235 Twin/Dbl
Jameson House: IR£190 Sgl.
IR£255 Twin/Dbl

Other Special Golf Packages:
2 B&B, and 1 golf, from IR£169.00 per person

DIRECTIONS

Portmarnock hotel and golf links is situated only 15 minutes by road from Dublin International Airport and under 30 minutes from the city centre itself.

Powerscourt Golf Club Apartments

*P*owerscourt is a free draining course with links characteristics. Built to championship standard, with top quality tees and exceptional tiered greens, it is set in some of Ireland's most beautiful parkland. The course has an abundance of mature trees and natural features, with stunning views to the sea and the Sugar Loaf Mountain.

Powerscourt Golf Club host to the 1998 Smurfit PGA Irish Championship. is situated within the magnificent 1000 acre Powercourt Estate in the Garden of Ireland just 12 miles south of Dublin city centre.

Studio apartments are available for accommodation on the Estate. Full of character they have been converted from original outbuildings adjacent to the main House. Either self-containing or with use of the full restaurant bar facilities at the Clubhouse, which is a short stroll away. Each self-contained apartment has twin/double beds, bath/shower, fully equipped kitchens, satellite TV, direct dial telephone. Guest enjoy free access to Waterfall gardens and the exhibition in the magnificent main house.

Powerscourt Golf Clubhouse has been constructed in Georgian style in keeping with Powerscourt House and the magnificent course.

Upstairs the beautifully proportioned function and dining room can seat up to 120 for a meal. Our Chef produces an imaginative bar menu and full a la carte menu in the restaurant.

GOLF INFORMATION

18-holes 6421 yards, par 72.
Parkland with links characteristics

Practice facilities: Practice ground.

GOlf Professional: Paul Thompson.
Tel: (01) 2046033

Instructions: Groups and individuals catered for.

Hire: Buggies and club hire.

CARD OF THE COURSE

1	401	Par 4	10	387	Par 4
2	461	Par 5	11	382	Par 4
3	154	Par 3	12	498	Par 5
4	332	Par 4	13	167	Par 3
5	216	Par 3	14	350	Par 4
6	484	Par 5	15	357	Par 4
7	383	Par 4	16	145	Par 3
8	422	Par 4	17	544	Par 5
9	348	Par 4	18	390	Par 4
Out	3201	Par 36	In	6421	Par 36

HOTEL INFORMATION

Powercourt Golf Club Apartments,
Powerscourt Golf Club,
Powerscourt Estate, Enniskerry. Co
Wicklow
Tel: (01) 204 6033
Fax: (01) 2761303

Rooms: 5 fully self contained apartments.
Rating: Bord Failte Approved.
Restaurants: Restaurant with full a la carte menu.
Childcare Facilities: Baby sitting can be organised.
Hair and Beauty: Powerscourt Springs Health Centre 2 ½ miles away.
Other Fitness Facilities: Powerscourt Springs Health Centre 2 ½ miles away.
Other Sporting Facilities: Tennis - Ennikerry village, swimming, skiing - Kilternan 1mile away.

TARIFF

B&B + 18 Holes
£99.00 per person.

Other Special Golfing Packages
Winter special £45.00 golf + 4 course dinner.

Weekend Breaks
£80.00 midweek per appartment per night.
£100.00 weekend per appartment per night.

DIRECTIONS

From Dublin - N11 to Loughlinstown Hospital roundabout straight on to M11, 4.5 miles to Enniskerry exit. Exit immediately after the bridge over M11, cross over M11 and return to Northbound lane exit first left on R117, 2.5 miles to Powerscourt. (alternate route through Dundrum and Kilteraen).

Rathsallagh House & Golf Club

Converted from Queen Anne stables in 1978, Rathsallagh is a large comfortable house situated in 530 acres of peaceful parkland with a walled garden and its own 18 hole championship golf course. Situated in West Co. Wicklow, one hour South of Dublin off the main Dublin Carlow road, Rathsallagh is central to some of the most beautiful countryside in eastern Ireland. Rathsallagh House has 17 bedrooms all en-suite bathrooms, restaurant, bar conference centre, 18 hole championship golf course, heated indoor swimming pool, sauna, billiard room, tennis, croquet, award winning walled garden.

Peter McEvoy and Christy O'Connor Jnr have created one of the best conditioned courses you will play anywhere. Built to USGA specifications, Rathsallagh is one of the more demanding parkland courses you are likely to play. Measuring close to 7,000 yards, Rathsallagh is not a course the high handicapper should play from the back tees. Anyone brave enough to play the course at its full length had better be a good player, a very good player.

The food is Country House cooking at its best and is organically produced by local growers and in Rathsallagh's gardens. Rathsallagh's restaurant has been recommended by international good food and hotel guides. Game in season and fresh fish from Ireland's coast line are specialities. Breakfast in Rathsallagh is an experience and has won the national Breakfast Award three times.

LOCAL ATTRACTIONS

One of the great things about Rathsallagh is that it is so close to Dublin. At 32 miles from the city centre, it's an easy hours drive, even in the worst traffic. Rathsallagh is convenient to The K Club, Druids Glen, Mount Juliet and Carlow for golf and also to the Curragh, Punchestown and Naas, for racing enthusiasts.

Horse riding, clay pigeon shooting, archery and hunting are available by prior arrangement.

GOLF INFORMATION

18 hole, 6916 yard parkland.
Par 72

Practice facilities: Covered outdoor driving range, short game two pitching greens, one putting green, three practice bunkers, video instruction.

Golf Professional: Brendan McDaid.

Instructions: Groups and individuals catered for.

Hire: Clubs and buggies

Green Fees: Weekday (Fri-Sun, Bank & Public Hols) £50.00, Weekends (Mon-Thur) £40.00, Early Bird (Before 9.30am Mon-Fri) £35.00

CARD OF THE COURSE					
1	571	Par 5	10	465	Par 4
2	454	Par 4	11	519	Par 5
3	400	Par 4	12	390	Par 4
4	173	Par 3	13	153	Par 3
5	396	Par 4	14	351	Par 4
6	502	Par 5	15	382	Par 4
7	176	Par 3	16	536	Par 5
8	382	Par 4	17	169	Par 3
9	447	Par 4	18	450	Par 4
Out 3501 Par 36			In 3415 Par 36		

HOTEL INFORMATION

Rathsallagh House & Golf Club
Dunlavin, West Wicklow
Tel: 00 353 (0)45-403112
Fax: 00 353 (0)45-403343
Rating: 4 Star Guesthouse.
Rooms: 17.
Restaurants: Country house cooking, game fish and beef specialities.
Hair and Beauty: By arrangement
Fitness Facilities: Swimming pool, sauna, billard table, tennis & croquet, claypigeon shooting by arrangement.
Other Sporting Facilities: By prior arrangement: Clay pigeon shooting, archery, fishing, deer stalking, fox hunting.
Other Leisure Activities: To be scheduled at a later date.

TARIFF

B&B from IR£55.00pps to IR£289.00pps per person sharing.

Special Golf Packages:
Two nights D/B&B including two rounds of golf from IR£289.00pp to IR£389.00pp

DIRECTIONS

From Dublin, take the N7 South to Naas via M50 from airport) Take the M7 Naas bypass South. Exit M7 for M9 Southbound. (The Kilcullen bypass) head South, signs direct to Carlow. After approx. 6 miles pass the Priory Inn on left. 2 miles on turn left at signpost for Rathsallagh. Rathsallagh sign posted from this junction.

Slieve Russell Hotel Golf & Country Club

*T*he Slieve Russell Hotel, Golf & Country Club combines the beswt of Irish hospitality with the finest of modern comfort.

The par 72 championship golf course has matured well over the years and has already decome one of the top golfing venues in Ireland. It is being compared to some of the great courses worldwide and in 1996 was the venue for the Smurfit Irish PGA Championship.

The 7013 yard course forms part of a 300 acre estate which includes 50 acres of lake and ponds. The unique style of the course is sensitively wrapped around the lakes and drumlins of the County Cavan landscape. Multiple tee positions facilitate all categiries of golfing ability with the championship tees demanding strategic shot making. A nine hole par 3 golf course and practice facility are also available. The Clubhouse, overlooking the course, incorporates the summit Bar and Restaurant, Golf Pro Shop and club storage area.

Located only 2 hours drive from both Dublin and belfast International Airports, the Slieve Russell is a complete resort with its leisure facilities in the Country Club, 151 superbly appointed bedrooms, a choice of Restaurants and Bars and a selection of purpose built and banqueting suites.

"The perfect location for business or pleasure".

LOCAL ATTRACTIONS

Cavan's long established reputation as one of Europe's premier fishing locations is a great attraction, while a canal cruise on the Shannon-Erne Waterway cannot be missed. Killykeen Forest Park with its forest clad islands, interwoven with lakes, is a natural reserve of staggering beauty.

On your list of places to see in County Fermanagh should be the magnificent Marble Arch Caves, Enniskillen Castle which houses the county museum, and the stately Florence Court mansion house.

Alternatively, you can simply enjoy the rugged and beautiful scenery in this unspolit part of Ireland.

GOLF INFORMATION

18 hole, 7053 yard parkland course

Par 72

Golf Professional: Liam McCool
Tel: 049 9526444

Practice facilities: Covered driving range.

Instructions: Groups and individuals catered for. Lessons and clinics may be booked on request.

Hire: Clubs, caddy cars and buggies.

Par 3 course and Driving Range also available

CARD OF THE COURSE					
1	428	Par 4	10	411	Par 4
2	434	Par 4	11	193	Par 3
3	398	Par 4	12	442	Par 4
4	167	Par 3	13	529	Par 5
5	436	Par 4	14	374	Par 4
6	512	Par 5	15	453	Par 4
7	220	Par 3	16	176	Par 3
8	389	Par 4	17	399	Par 4
9	552	Par 5	18	540	Par 5
Out	3536	Par 36	In	3517	Par 36

HOTEL INFORMATION

Slieve Russell Hotel,
Golf & Country Club
Ballyconnell, Co. Cavan
Tel: 049 26444
Fax: 049 26046
Rating: 4 Star Hotel.
Rooms: 151.
Restaurants: Conall Cearnach Restaurant – sophisticated atmosphere/Brackley Restaurant – less formal.
Childcare Facilities: Younger guests are well taken care of in the creche and the ever popular 'Kiddies Klub' which is run during holiday times.
Hair and Beauty: Hair & Beauty Salon in Hotel.
Fitness Facilities: Five star range of leisure and sporting facilities with 20m swimming pool, jacuzzi, steamroom, sauna and fitness suite.
Other Sporting Facilities: Snooker room, games room, 2 squash courts and 4 all weather tennis courts.

TARIFF

Weekend
from £165.00 per person sharing – **2 B&B** and 1 Evening meal.

Special Golf Packages:
B&B including 18 holes available on request.

Other Special Golf Packages:
Available on request.

DIRECTIONS

From Dublin, follow the N3 through Navan and Cavan town to Belturbet and then follow the signs to Ballyconnell village. From Belfast, follow the M1 leading to the A4, through Five Mile Town, Lisnaskea, Derrylin and Ballconnell. The hotel is situated 1 mile past Ballyconnell.

BALLYMASCANLON GOLF & LEISURE CLUB

Dundalk, Co. Louth, Ireland. Tel: +353 (0)42 9371124 Fax: +353 (0)42 9371598
Web: www.globalgolf.com/ballymascanlon Email: info@ballymascanlon.com

18 HOLES	**PAR** 68	**5548 YARDS**

TYPE OF GOLF COURSE: Parkland

RATING: 3 Star

B&B + 18 HOLES: £55.00pp sharing

OTHER SPECIAL GOLF PACKAGES:
On request

Nestled in 130 acres of private parkland estate, an impressive Victorian house forms the heart of this magnificent facility. The house has been transformed into a modern hotel offering luxury accommodation and serving food of the highest standard. At Ballymascanlon House Hotel all activities are catered for. In the superb health club you can relax or workout to your preference. Alternatively you can walk the grounds and enjoy the historic scenery. Then of course, there is the magnificent 18 hole parkland golf course designed by internationally renowned Craddock & Ruddy, which should more than please. Set amidst the historic cooly landscape the course is as challenging as it is rewarding. A golfer's dream!.

3 miles north of Dundalk on main Dublin-Belfast road, take 3rd exit off roundabout, drive along Carlingford Road - Ballymascanlon Hotel is on the left.

CITYWEST HOTEL, CONFERENCE LEISURE & GOLF RESORT

Saggart, Co. Dublin. Tel: 00353 1 4010500 Fax: 00353 1 4588565 Email: info@citywest-hotel.iol.ie

18 HOLES	**PAR** 70	**6691 YARDS**

TYPE OF GOLF COURSE: Parkland
GOLF PROFESSIONALS: George Henry P.G.A, Martin Levng P.G.A UK, Karl Holmes P.G.A, Giles Rebuffel P.G.A France
TEL: 003531-4587011
B&B + 18 HOLES: 2B&B + 1 dinner £99.00p.p.s Residential golf £22.00
OTHER SPECIAL GOLF PACKAGES:
Early Bird: 7.00am - 10.00am - Breakfast + 1 round of golf - £25.00p.p
Twilight - Golf: 9 holes - £15.00p.p

Citywest Hotel, with 200 guestrooms and suites and set in over 180 acres of majestic woodland is located just minutes from the city centre. Our Health & Leisure Club with 20m swimming pool offers a state of the art gymnasium, extensive Spa facilities and a range of hair & beauty treatments.

Our Championship Golf Course designed by Christy O'Connor Jnr., is recognised as being one of the most outstanding courses being played at international level.

The on-site MacGregor Academy offers expert tuition and advice, which can be put into practice on the Floodlit Driving Range.

The Terrace Restaurant, is a gourmet dining experience, whilst our busy Bars and Lounges, make the ideal meeting place for locals and visitors alike.

DEER PARK HOTEL & GOLF COURSES

Howth Co. Dublin, Ireland. Tel: INT + 353-1-8322624 Fax: INT + 353-1-8392405

36 HOLES	**PAR** 72/72	**6830/6503 YARDS**

TYPE OF GOLF COURSE: Parkland

RATING: Bord Failte (I.T.B) and RAC 3 Star

B&B + 18 HOLES: £60.00 per person

OTHER SPECIAL GOLF PACKAGES:
£126 – 2 nights B&B, 1 dinner and 2 days golf.

This is Ireland's largest golf complex set in 600 acres, just 9 miles from Dublin City and the Airport. All rooms are en-suite with telephone satellite TV and tea/coffee facilities. There is an a-la-carte restaurant, bar and indoor swimming pool.

The golf facilities comprise two 18-hole full courses, a 12-hole short course and an 18-hole pitch and putt.

KILKEA CASTLE HOTEL & GOLF CLUB
Castledermot, Co. Kildare. Tel: 0503 45555 Fax: 0503 45505.

Another of Ireland's country estates turned into a golf course and hotel, Kilkea Castle is one of the oldest inhabited castles in Ireland. It sits on River Griese, and the river serves as a hazard for many of the holes on the accompanying golf course.

Being one of Ireland's oldest, the castle has a lot of history attached to it. It is a 39 bedroom hotel where the service and accommodation is five star. Throw in the excellent leisure facilities and you have a very good golf complex in the heart of County Kildare.

18 HOLES	PAR 70	6700 YARDS

TYPE OF GOLF COURSE: Parkland

GREEN FEES:

Weekdays: IR£25.

Weekend: IR£25

MOUNT JULIET
Thomastown, Co. Kilkenny. Ireland. Tel: 353 56 73000 Fax: 353 56 73019

Deep amid the rolling green hills of Ireland's beautiful south east, lies Mount Juliet. Twelfth century origins, a leisurely pace of life and traditionally generous hospitality combine with world-class sporting and conference facilities. Enjoy golf, horse riding, fishing, shooting, tennis, clay target shooting, 18 hole putting course the spa and leisure centre, or simply relax in the idyllic surroundings.

18 HOLES	PAR 72	7142 YARDS

TYPE OF GOLF COURSE: Parkland
HOTEL RATING: 4 Star AA/RAC Gold
Ribbon 4 Stars/Irish Tourist Board 4 Stars
GOLF PROFESSIONAL: Ted Higgins
TEL: 353 56 73000
B&B + 18 HOLES: From £147.50
(high season weekend)
OTHER SPECIAL GOLF PACKAGES:
Early Bird – Sunsetter – Group rates on request

NUREMORE HOTEL
Carrickmacross, Co. Monaghan, Ireland. Tel: 00 358 42 9661438 or 00353 42 9664016
Fax: 00 353 42 9661853

Country house hotel comprising 72 bedrooms and many leisure and conference facilities including 18 hole golf course, 18m swimming pool, whirlpool, steam room and sauna, squash court, snooker, conference facilities for 2-500 people.

18 HOLES	PAR 71	5870 METERS

TYPE OF GOLF COURSE: Parkland

HOTEL RATING: AA Bord Failte

GOLF PROFESSIONAL: Maurice Cassidy
TEL: 00 358 42 9661438

B&B + 18 HOLES: £140 + £25

Lismore Castle, Co. Waterford

ST. HELENS BAY GOLF & COUNTRY CLUB
St. Helens Bay, Rosslare Harbour, Co. Wexford. Tel: 053 33669/33234 Fax: 053 33803

Irish cottages overlooking beach beside the golf course. Designed by Philip Walton and containing all the usual facilities including bar, dining room and tennis courts etc. Specialists in society golf groups.

18 HOLES	PAR 72	6800 YARDS

TYPE OF GOLF COURSE: Links & Parkland

RATING: 3 Star

B&B + 18 HOLES: £45.00/£50.00

OTHER SPECIAL GOLF PACKAGES:
Will quote you for 7,5 or 3 day Golf Breaks and hosts 6-3 day golf classics during each year.

CHARLESLAND GOLF & COUNTRY CLUB
Greystone, Co. Wicklow. Tel: +353-1-2874350
Fax: +353-1-2874360

HOLES: 18	YARDS: 6162	PAR: 72

FERNHILL GOLF & COUNTRY CLUB
Carrigdive, Co. Cork, Ireland Tel: 021 372226
Fax: 021 371011

HOLES: 18	YARDS: 6241	PAR: 69

FITZPATRICKS HOTEL
Silver Springs, Tivoli, Cork, Ireland
Tel: 00353 21 507533 Fax: 00353 21 505128

HOLES: 9	YARDS: 2000m	PAR: 32

LEE VALLEY GOLF & COUNTRY CLUB
Clashanure, Ovens, County Cork, Ireland
Tel: 00353 21 331721 Fax: 00353 21 331695

HOLES: 18	YARDS: 6434	PAR: 72

WATERFORD CASTLE
The Island, Ballinakill, Waterford, Ireland
Tel: 00353 51 871633 Fax: 00353 51 871634

HOLES: 18	YARDS: 6209m	PAR: 72

Index

Index

Spoilt for c

From Britain's leading golf book publisher, the complete guides to the finest courses of Great Britain, Ireland and now... Florida

Each *Golfing Gems* edition gives you 72 wonderful, sometimes lesser-known but accessible, courses to play. Unlike other guides, no charge is made to the Clubs for their inclusion as entries are allocated purely on merit. Color photographs and an extensive editorial commentary on each course make these an essential addition to any golfers library.

Golfing Breaks is the only comprehensive guide to the golf resorts of Britain and Ireland. Many feature photographs of the course and hotel, a description of the facilities on offer and key information for the visitor including local places of interest.

Look for them in all good bookstores.

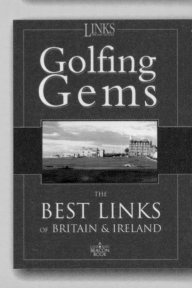

ice!

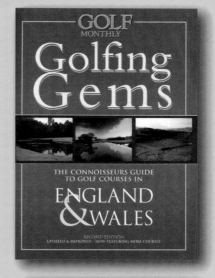
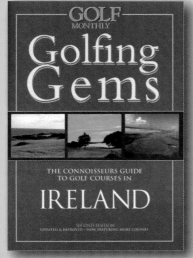
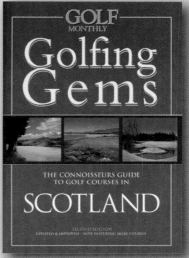